HOME ECONOMICS
for CCEA GCSE

Nicola Anderson Claire Thomson

Acknowledgements

The publishers thank the following for permission to reproduce copyright material: British Nutrition Foundation (**pp.19, 42, 89**); the Consumer Council for Northern Ireland (**pp.91, 107, 112, 113, 121**); Institute of Grocery Distribution (**p.19**). The following Crown Copyright material is reproduced under the terms of the Click-Use licence: eatwell plate (**p.6**), 8 tips (**p.8**), BMI chart (**p.52**), information on food allergies (**p.62–3**) – all Food Standards Agency; EARs (**p.58**) – Department of Health, Dietary Reference Values for Food Energy and Nutrients, HMSO.

Thanks are also due to the following for permission to reproduce photographs and other images: Advice NI: **p.118**; British Heart Foundation: **p.22b**; Citizens Advice: **p.119**; Corbis: **pp.68r** (Ashley Cooper), **73l** (Image Source), **78** (Jim Richardson), **99ct** (Pixland); Department of Enterprise, Trade and Investment: **p.122**; Diabetes UK Campaign: **p.45t**; Dreamstime: **pp.7/16b** (Chode), **10tr** (Felixcoinc), **11c** (Looby), **11b** (Griffin024), **12b** (Robert Anthony), **25/26t/27/76b** (Hsandler), **28** (Photo-euphoria), **33b/34/35t** (Monkey business images), **37** (David Calicchio), **46** (Jarenwick-lund), **49** (Sheftsoff), **57** (Photosoup), **62** (Elena Elisseeva), **68l** (Monkey business images), **68c** (Celwell), **69t** (Monkey business images), **73r** (Rmarmion), **74** (Palangsi), **85tl** (Elena Elisseeva), **85bl** (Og-vision), **85br** (Monkey business images), **96l** (Aqua land photos), **96r** (Monkey business images), **104t** (Qwasyx), **105t** (Ngothyeaun), **105cl** (Kamchatka), **105bl** (Edward Bock), **108b** (Andreblais), **1131** (Monkey business images); Dreamstime (micro-stock): **p.41** (Eraxion); Fairtrade Foundation: **p.95** (Marcus Lyon); Getty Images: **pp.4t** (Image Source), **98ct** (Peter Macdiarmid), **98b** (Joe Fox), **99cb** (Rubberball); Istock: box border (adapted; Liquid-planet), **pp.4b** (Sean Locke), **9l** (Graca Victoria), **9r** (Norbert - Zsolt Suto), **10tl** (Monika Adamczyk), **10b** (Paul Cowan), **14** (Donald Gruener), **15t** (Ivan Bajic), **15c** (hywit dimyadi), **15b** (Monika Adamczyk), **26b/29b/30/33t/35b/36/38/59/60/64** (adapted; Ryan Osbrink), **29t/76t** (Damir Cudic), **31** (Carmen Martinez Banus), **39/76c** (Alexander Raths), **45b** (Sofiia Kravchenko), **56** (adapted; Brian Smith), **63** (Diane Labombarbe), **65** (Linda & Colin McKie), **66, 71** (adapted; Brian Smith), **75t** (Stephen Dumayne), **82, 99b** (Jim Jurica), **104br** (Aleksandar-Pal Sakala), **108t, 110** (Xaviarnau); Oxford Designers and Illustrators: **p.40**; Photolibrary: **pp.7t** (Maximilian Stock Ltd), **7/12t** (Rosenfeld), **7/16t/55b** (Maximilian Stock Ltd), **32, 47** (Medicimage), **51** (Coll-Paul Simcock), **55t** (Nucleus Inc), **69r** (Robert Lawson), **70cl** (Tim Hill), **70cr** (Robert Lawson), **70b** (Robert Lawson), **73c** (Graham Kirk), **83** (Robert Lawson), **85tc** (Acevedo Melanie), **85tr** (Kathryn Russell), **85bc** (Heather Brown), **86** (Tim Hawley), **97** (Alexandr Labetskly), **98t** (Wojtek Buss), **98cb** (RAF MAKDA), **99t** (Michael Weber), **104bl** (Mark Williamson), **105br** (Doco Dalfiano), **109t** (Nova-stock); Science Photo Library: **p.71**; Vegetarian Society: **p. 23**. Photographs on **pp.20-21** by Carole Binding and on **p.70t, 72** by Mike Nason. Illustrations on **pp.48, 58, 67, 75b, 84, 87, 90, 94, 101, 102–3, 106, 108, 109, 112–13, 114, 115,** and others adapted, by Carole Binding.

Orders: please contact Bookpoint Ltd, 130 Milton Park, Abingdon, Oxon OX14 4SB. Telephone: (44) 01235 827720. Fax: (44) 01235 400454. Lines are open 9.00–5.00, Monday to Saturday, with a 24-hour message answering service. Visit our website at www.hoddereducation.co.uk

First published in 2009 by
Hodder Education,
An Hachette UK Company
338 Euston Road, London NW1 3BH

Impression number 5 4 3 2 1
Year 2013 2012 2011 2010 2009

Cover photo: *Main image*, © Jean Maurice/Red Cover/Getty Images; *t–b*, © Photodisc/Getty Images, Alex Segre/Alamy, © Fotolia.com

Produced for Hodder Education by White-Thomson Publishing Ltd
Editor: Ruth Nason; Design and illustrative work: Carole Binding
Printed in Italy

A catalogue record for this title is available from the British Library

ISBN: 978 0340 985045

Contents

Introduction

The two parts of this course help you to understand the dietary needs of different family members and to become a discerning consumer.

This Student's Book has been written to follow the subject content of the CCEA GCSE specification in Home Economics.

GCSE Home Economics is divided into two parts:

- Diet and Health
- Consumer Awareness.

DIET AND HEALTH

In this part of the course you will develop the knowledge, understanding and skills needed for providing healthy diets for family members throughout life. You will learn that people of different ages have different dietary needs and that food choice is affected by social, economic, environmental, cultural, physiological and psychological factors.

CONSUMER AWARENESS

This part of the course enables you to apply knowledge, understanding and skills as discerning and effective managers of resources. You will learn to recognise how choices can be influenced by personal, social, cultural, economic and environmental factors.

ABOUT THE BOOK

The chapter titles in this book match the list of contents of the GCSE specification. Each chapter begins with a list of its learning outcomes and includes a range of activities, which are designed to help you meet the assessment objectives outlined on page 5. Terms shown in ***bold italics*** the first time they appear in the text are explained in the Glossary.

ASSESSMENT

In GCSE Home Economics, students are assessed against three assessment objectives (AO). You must be able to:

- AO1: recall, select and communicate knowledge and understanding of a range of contexts
- AO2: apply skills, knowledge and understanding in a variety of contexts and in planning and carrying out investigations and tasks
- AO3: analyse and evaluate information, sources and evidence, make reasoned judgements and present conclusions.

The skills required to meet these objectives are developed during your two-year GCSE course and are assessed as this table shows.

Content	Assessment	Weighting
Unit 1: Diet and Health and Consumer Awareness	External assessment (compulsory) Format: 1 hour 30 minutes examination (single tier) The examination has two sections: • Section A: Diet and Health • Section B: Consumer Awareness. Both sections include short-answer questions, structured questions and extended-response questions that require extended writing. All questions are compulsory.	40%
Unit 2: Diet and Health (controlled assessment)	Internal assessment (compulsory) Format: One controlled assessment task consisting of: • a planning activity • a practical activity • an evaluation activity.	40%
Unit 3: Consumer Awareness (controlled assessment)	Internal assessment (compulsory) Format: One controlled assessment task including: • identification of issues • research-based activity • primary investigation • conclusions and evaluation.	20%

What's on the plate?

In this chapter you will learn about the 'eatwell plate' devised by the Food Standards Agency. After studying the chapter, you should be able to:

- explain how the 'eatwell plate' helps consumers achieve a healthy and well-balanced diet
- identify the main nutrients provided by each food group
- discuss the '8 tips for eating well' (Food Standards Agency) as a way of helping consumers achieve a healthy and well-balanced diet.

The 'eatwell plate'. It is produced by the Food Standards Agency, an independent government department which works to protect the public's health and consumer interests in relation to health.

Consumers are exposed to a wide range of information about healthy eating, and over time this can become confusing. The 'eatwell plate' was produced by the Food Standards Agency as a tool to make healthy eating easier to understand.

The agency wants to ensure that people receive a consistent message about healthy eating. Therefore it encourages organisations and individuals to use the 'eatwell plate' when planning diets to maximise health and well-being.

ACTIVITY 1

a Keep a personal food diary, recording details of the foods and drinks you have consumed over a period of time. Remember to include snacks.

b Use the information you have recorded to compare your diet to the 'eatwell plate'.

c Evaluate your diet. Think about the following questions.
- Does your diet include foods from each food group?
- Does your diet include foods from each food group in the correct proportions?
- Do you need to make any changes to your diet? Explain the changes you could make to achieve a healthy, well-balanced diet.

The 'eatwell plate' helps consumers by making it easy to see the types and proportions of different foods needed to achieve a healthy and well-balanced diet. Foods are divided into the following five groups, which are represented on the plate:

- bread, rice, potatoes, pasta and other starchy foods
- fruit and vegetables
- meat, fish, eggs, beans and other non-dairy sources of protein
- milk and dairy foods
- foods and drinks high in fat and/or sugar.

A healthy and well-balanced diet consists of a range of foods from each of the five groups, in the correct proportions as shown on the 'eatwell plate'. Starchy foods and fruit and vegetables are the two largest food groups on the plate. This means that more of these foods should be included in the diet than foods from the other groups. Foods and drinks high in fat and/or sugar make up the smallest group on the plate and should be eaten less often, in smaller amounts.

While it may not be possible to achieve this at every meal, it is important that the overall balance of your diet is right.

NUTRIENTS PROVIDED BY EACH FOOD GROUP

Food provides nutrients, which the body needs to stay alive and work well. No single food provides all the nutrients required and so it is essential to eat a balanced diet, with a range of foods from all the food groups. Table 1.1 shows the main nutrients provided by foods in each food group.

Table 1.1: The five food groups and the nutrients they provide

Food group	Main nutrients provided by foods in the food group		
Bread, rice, potatoes, pasta and other starchy foods	Carbohydrate	B group vitamins	Calcium
Fruit and vegetables	Carbohydrate	Vitamin C Vitamin A	Water
Meat, fish, eggs, beans and other non-dairy protein sources	Protein Fat	Vitamin D	Iron
Milk and dairy foods	Calcium Protein	Fat Vitamin D	Water
Foods and drinks high in fat and/or sugar	Carbohydrate	Fat	

8 TIPS FOR EATING WELL

The Food Standards Agency has identified '8 tips for eating well'. These are:

1. Base your meals on starchy foods.
2. Eat lots of fruit and vegetables.
3. Eat more fish – including a portion of oily fish each week.
4. Cut down on ***saturated fat*** and sugar.
5. Try to eat less salt – no more than 6 g a day.
6. Get active and try to be a healthy weight.
7. Drink plenty of water.
8. Don't skip breakfast.

The Food Standards Agency suggests that the two keys to a healthy diet are:

- eating the right amount of food for how active you are
- eating a range of foods to ensure you are getting a balanced diet.

This is the front of the Food Standards Agency's leaflet which explains the tips for eating well. You will need this leaflet for activity 2.

ACTIVITY 2

a Divide into eight groups. Each group will focus on a different one of the '8 tips for eating well'.

b For this activity, you will need to read the Food Standards Agency's leaflet, '8 tips for making healthier choices'. You can download it from www.food.gov.uk/multimedia/pdfs/eatwell0708.pdf

c In your group, gather information so that you can present the following to the rest of the class:

- the reason why the tip is important for healthy eating
- suggestions for putting the tip into practice
- recipes that could be used, or modified, to meet the advice of the '8 tips for eating well'
- specific groups of people for whom the tip is particularly relevant, for example, people in certain age stages or people with dietary disorders.

d Decide what will be the most appropriate method for presenting the information you have collected. You could produce a fact sheet, poster, PowerPoint® presentation, information leaflet or note-making grid. It is important that the information you share is accurate and clearly presented.

e Your group could plan, make and evaluate a meal or a menu which demonstrates how your chosen tip for eating well can be put into practice.

Chapter 2

What's in food?

In this chapter you will learn about the following nutrients: carbohydrate, fat, protein, minerals (sodium, calcium, iron), vitamins (A, D, B group, C) and water. After studying the chapter, you should be able to:

- identify valuable sources of nutrients and explain the functions of each nutrient
- explain the effects on health of deficiency and excess of each nutrient
- explain the use of Guideline Daily Amounts (GDAs) in planning healthy balanced diets
- discuss these nutrition essentials:
  - protein: biological value and complementation
  - fat: saturated and unsaturated
  - carbohydrate: soluble and insoluble non-starch polysaccharides (NSP)
  - vitamins and minerals: links between vitamin C and iron, vitamin D and calcium; factors maximising availability of calcium and iron.

Diet refers to the food we eat or drink. A balanced diet containing food from all sections of the 'eatwell plate' is central to overall good health. In order to plan a balanced diet, it is important to understand that all foods provide a range of nutrients necessary for good health. Poor diet choices can have an adverse impact on health, leading to disorders such as ***iron deficiency anaemia***, ***obesity***, ***coronary heart disease***, ***hypertension***, ***diabetes***, ***dental caries*** and ***osteoporosis***.

This chapter outlines the main functions and sources of the nutrients required for optimal health.

CARBOHYDRATES

The main function of carbohydrate is to provide the body with energy. There are two main types of carbohydrate:

- sugars, which are ***simple carbohydrates***
- starches, which are more ***complex carbohydrates***.

The difference between the two types is important. Sugars are absorbed quickly by the body, and raise blood sugar levels rapidly. Starches take longer to digest and absorb. They have a positive impact on keeping blood sugar levels constant.

The body needs a constant supply of carbohydrate to meet its energy requirements. About 50 per cent of dietary energy should come from carbohydrates. If the diet is low in carbohydrate, the body uses protein for energy instead. This then means that less protein is available for the growth and repair of body tissues.

Sugary foods, such as a chocolate caramel bar, and starchy foods, such as pasta, are two different sources of carbohydrate.

Non-starch polysaccharide (NSP)

A third type of carbohydrate is ***non-starch polysaccharide (NSP)***. This is found only in plants. Unlike the other carbohydrates, NSP is not absorbed but is needed to keep the digestive system healthy.

There are two main types of NSP: insoluble and soluble. Table 2.1 shows that they have different functions. This means that it is important to eat a variety of foods, rich in both types of NSP, to maximise benefits to health.

Table 2.1: The functions and sources of the two types of non-starch polysaccharides (NSP)

Insoluble NSP	Soluble NSP
• Assists digestion. • Helps prevent constipation. • Is filling and can decrease the need to eat between meals, helping to maintain a healthy weight. Sources of insoluble NSP include wholegrain cereals and wholemeal bread, wholemeal flour, pasta and brown rice.	• Helps reduce ***blood cholesterol levels***. • Helps to control blood sugar levels. Sources of soluble NSP include oats, fruit, vegetables and pulses, for example, beans, lentils and chickpeas.

Wholemeal bread and lentil soup are sources of NSP. This meal is also an example of protein complementation, which is explained on page 12.

ACTIVITY 1

When you have studied the whole of this chapter, answer these questions on carbohydrates.

a Complete a glossary for the following diet and health terms:
- sugars
- starches
- non-starch polysaccharide (NSP)
- insoluble NSP
- soluble NSP
- intrinsic sugars
- extrinsic sugars
- milk sugars
- non-milk extrinsic sugars (NMES).

b How much energy does 1g of carbohydrate provide?

c Outline the different functions of sugar and starch.

d Identify the percentage of dietary energy that should be provided by carbohydrate and explain why meeting this target is so important.

e Why is it important to eat a variety of foods rich in insoluble and soluble NSP?

f What is the 'protein-sparing effect' of carbohydrate?

g Why is it important to reduce consumption of non-milk extrinsic sugars (NMES)?

FAT

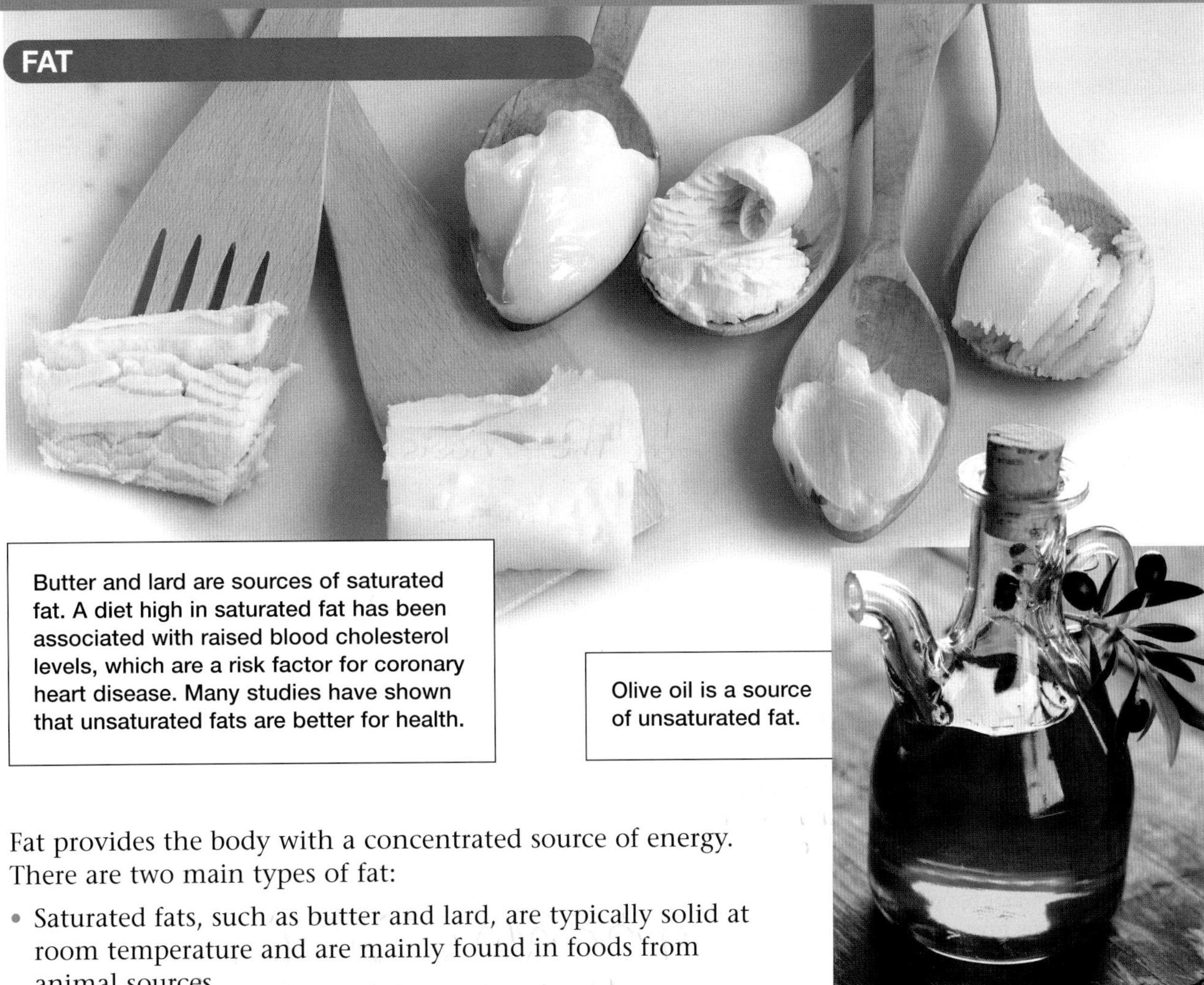

Butter and lard are sources of saturated fat. A diet high in saturated fat has been associated with raised blood cholesterol levels, which are a risk factor for coronary heart disease. Many studies have shown that unsaturated fats are better for health.

Olive oil is a source of unsaturated fat.

Fat provides the body with a concentrated source of energy. There are two main types of fat:

- Saturated fats, such as butter and lard, are typically solid at room temperature and are mainly found in foods from animal sources.
- ***Unsaturated fats***, such as olive oil or sunflower oil, are typically liquid at room temperature and are mainly from plant sources.

Fats are composed of fatty acids. The body can make all of the fatty acids it needs except for two, known as ***Omega 3*** and ***Omega 6***. These are called ***essential fatty acids (EFAs)*** and must be provided in the diet.

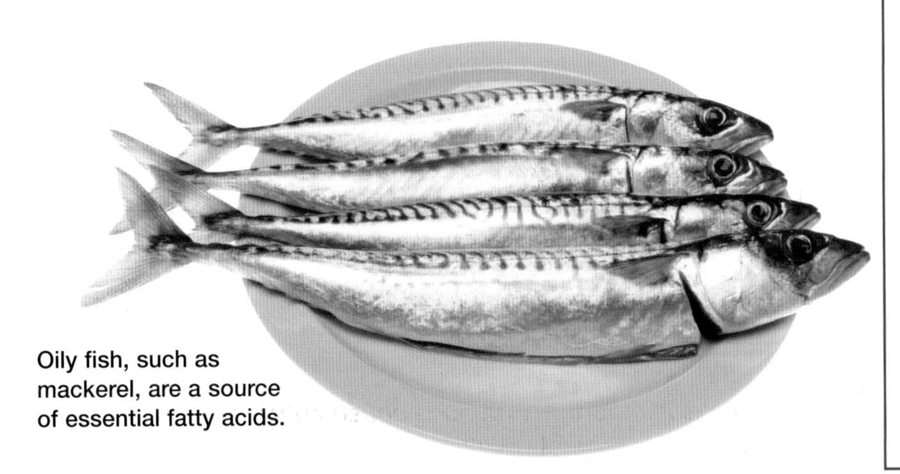

Oily fish, such as mackerel, are a source of essential fatty acids.

ACTIVITY 2

When you have studied the whole of this chapter, answer these questions on fat.

a How much energy does 1g of fat provide?
b Outline two differences between saturated and unsaturated fat.
c Identify two food sources of saturated fat and two food sources of unsaturated fat.
d Why is it important to include foods rich in Omega 3 and Omega 6 in the diet?
e Identify two food sources of essential fatty acids (EFAs).
f State two consequences on health of eating excess fat.

ACTIVITY 3

When you have studied the whole of this chapter, answer these questions on protein.

a How much energy does 1g of protein provide?
b State three functions of protein.
c What are amino acids?
d Describe the difference between dispensable and indispensable amino acids.
e What is protein quality and why is it so important?
f List two food sources of LBV and HBV protein.
g Explain the complementary action of proteins.

PROTEIN

Proteins are the basis of body structures such as muscles, skin and hair. They are composed of ***amino acids***. The body needs amino acids to produce new body tissues and to repair damaged tissues. Amino acids are classified as:

- dispensable amino acids, which can be produced in the body
- indispensable amino acids, which cannot be made in the body and so must be provided by the diet.

Humans need about twenty amino acids, and about ten of these are indispensable.

The quality of the protein eaten is important and depends on the amino acids that are present. If a food contains all the indispensable amino acids in the approximate proportions required by humans, it is said to have a high biological value (HBV). A food that lacks one or more of the indispensable amino acids is said to have a low biological value (LBV).

All these foods are sources of protein. Proteins from animal sources have a higher biological value than proteins from plant sources. The exceptions to this rule are gelatine, an animal protein with low biological value (LBV), and soya, a plant protein with high biological value (HBV).

Complementary action of protein

LBV proteins lack one or more of the indispensable amino acids. This is called the limiting amino acid and it varies in different proteins. When two LBV protein foods, such as a pulse and a cereal, are eaten at a meal (for example, beans on toast, or lentil soup with bread), the amino acids in one food will compensate for the limiting amino acid of the other, resulting in a meal of high biological value. This is known as complementation (the complementary action of proteins).

Complementation is particularly relevant for people who exclude animal products from their diet, for example, vegetarians and ***vegans***. As long as these people eat a variety of LBV proteins in combination, the quality of their protein intake can be as good as that of someone who eats HBV foods.

Separately, baked beans and toast each have a low biological value. But combining them results in a meal of high biological value.

NUTRIENTS AND THEIR ROLES

Nutrients have specific roles in helping to achieve optimal health. Table 2.2 summarises the main functions and sources of carbohydrate, fat and protein and highlights the impact on health of deficiency and excess of these nutrients. It is important to develop your knowledge of this information and to be able to apply it throughout your study of Diet and Health.

Table 2.2: The functions and sources of carbohydrate, fat and protein, and the effects of having too little or too much of them in the diet

Nutrient	Functions	Sources	Deficiency	Excess
Carbohydrate	• Provides energy (1g provides 3.75 ***kcal***) • Has protein-sparing effect (so protein is used for growth and repair rather than energy) • Non-starch polysaccharides (NSP) help to: - prevent constipation - lower blood cholesterol levels - keep blood sugar levels constant	**Sugars** • Intrinsic sugars (found in the cellular structure of foods): in whole fruits and vegetables • Extrinsic sugars (not found in the cellular structure of foods): - milk sugars in dairy products - ***non-milk extrinsic sugars (NMES)*** in honey, fruit juices, table sugar, confectionery **Starch**, in potatoes, bread, rice, pasta	Low NSP intake is associated with: • constipation • some gut diseases such as diverticulitis and bowel cancer	• Frequent consumption of food and drinks containing NMES can increase risk of dental caries • Too much energy (kcal) can lead to excess weight gain and obesity
Fat	• Provides energy (1g provides 9 kcal) • Keeps us warm • Insulates and protects organs • Important in forming structure of body cells • Source of fat-soluble vitamins A and D • Source of Omega 3 and Omega 6	**Saturated fat** • Found in meat, eggs, dairy products, butter **Unsaturated fat** • Found in olive oil, sunflower oil, olives, avocados **Essential fatty acids** • Found in oily fish, margarine, nuts, seeds	Deficiency is rare	• Can lead to high blood cholesterol levels, a risk factor for coronary heart disease • Too much energy (kcal) can lead to excess weight gain and obesity
Protein	• Needed for growth and for repair of body tissues • Can be used as a secondary source of energy (1g provides 4 kcal)	**Animal protein** • Found in meat, fish, eggs, dairy products **Plant protein** • Found in cereal products, nuts, pulses **Novel protein** • Tofu, soya products	• Can delay growth in children • ***Protein energy malnutrition*** occurs in developing countries and mainly affects young children	Excess is rare

MINERALS

Minerals are essential nutrients that the body needs in small amounts. They have many different functions, but in general they are protective and help to keep us healthy. Table 2.3 summarises the main functions and sources of the minerals sodium, calcium and iron and highlights the impact on health of deficiency and excess of each.

A healthy diet includes no more than 6g of salt per day (3g per day for children).

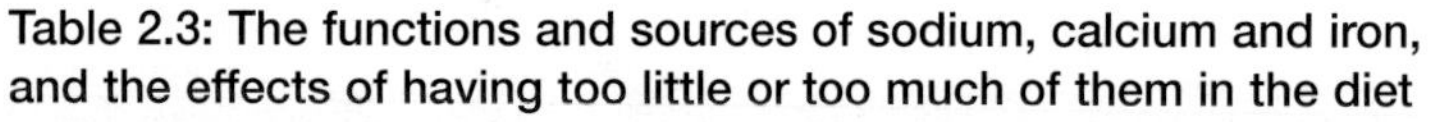

Table 2.3: The functions and sources of sodium, calcium and iron, and the effects of having too little or too much of them in the diet

Nutrient	Functions	Sources	Deficiency	Excess
Sodium	• Helps to keep body fluids balanced • Maintains nerve function	• Table salt • Salty snacks, e.g. crisps or peanuts • ***Processed foods***, e.g. some types of ready meals, meat products, breakfast cereals	Deficiency is rare	• Is linked with an increase in high ***blood pressure*** (hypertension) • Increases the risk of ***strokes*** and coronary heart disease
Calcium	• Important for the formation of bones and teeth • Necessary for nerve and muscle function • Involved in blood clotting	• Milk, cheese and other dairy foods • Green leafy vegetables such as broccoli and cabbage • Soya beans, tofu, soya drinks with added calcium • Nuts • White bread • Fish where bones are eaten, e.g. sardines	• Can reduce ***peak bone mass***, which is a contributory factor in the development of osteoporosis in later life	Excess is rare
Iron	• Needed to form ***haemoglobin*** in red blood cells, which transport oxygen around the body • Boosts energy stores • Needed for normal functioning of the ***immune system***	**Haem iron** (mainly from animal sources, easily absorbed by the body) • meat, liver **Non-haem iron** (mainly from plant sources, not as easily absorbed by the body) • beans, nuts, dried fruit, fortified breakfast cereals, green leafy vegetables, eggs	• Leads to low iron stores in the body and eventually to iron deficiency anaemia	• Very high doses can be fatal, particularly to children, so iron supplements should be avoided at this stage of life

ACTIVITY 4

Answer the following questions on minerals.

a Outline two functions of sodium.
b State the consequences to health of excess sodium in the diet.
c List three foods high in sodium.
d Outline two functions of calcium.
e State the consequences to health of a deficiency of calcium in the diet.
f List three food sources of calcium.
g Outline two functions of iron.
h State the consequences to health of a deficiency of iron in the diet.
i Differentiate between haem and non-haem iron.
j Identify two food sources of haem and non-haem iron.

Calcium from yogurt is more easily absorbed than calcium from spinach.

Absorbing calcium

Calcium is most easily absorbed from milk and dairy products. It is less easily absorbed from plant foods. Calcium absorption may be reduced by the presence of phytates in plant foods (for example, cereals and pulses) and by the presence of oxalates in vegetables and fruit (for example, spinach and rhubarb).

The way that calcium is absorbed by the body is partly controlled by vitamin D (see pages 16–17). A lack of vitamin D can reduce the amount of calcium that the body absorbs. This can affect bone health and contribute to the development of osteoporosis.

Absorbing iron

Vitamin C in the orange juice helps absorption of iron from the cereal.

Iron from animal sources, known as 'haem iron', is absorbed more effectively than iron from plant sources.

Absorption of non-haem iron from plant sources is affected by various factors. NSP, phytate in cereals or pulses and tannins in tea can reduce absorption of non-haem iron.

Eating food containing vitamin C at the same time as food containing iron from non-haem sources can help the body to absorb the iron. Examples are to have fruit juice or fruit with ***fortified*** breakfast cereal, vegetables with beans, or nuts with rice.

ACTIVITY 5

Answer the following questions on vitamins.

a Identify the fat-soluble and water-soluble vitamins.
b Why is it important not to consume an excessive amount of foods rich in fat-soluble vitamins? Does this advice apply to water-soluble vitamins?
c Which two vitamins are antioxidants?
d List three functions of vitamin C.
e Write down three dietary sources of vitamin B_{12}.
f An excess of which vitamin could cause miscarriage?
g Describe the link between vitamin D, rickets and osteomalacia.
h Identify two plant and two animal sources of vitamin A.
i What is the main function of vitamin B_1?
j Outline the consequences of a diet deficient in folate.
k Why should foods rich in vitamin C and iron be eaten together?
l Identify three factors that affect the absorption of calcium.

VITAMINS

Vitamins are essential nutrients that are needed in very small amounts. Usually only a few milligrams (mg) or micrograms (mcg) are needed per day. Most vitamins cannot be made by the body and have to be provided by the diet. An exception is vitamin D, which can be obtained by the action of sunlight on the skin.

There are two types of vitamins.

- The fat-soluble vitamins are vitamins A and D. They are found mainly in fatty foods from animal sources, such as butter, lard, dairy foods, liver and oily fish. Although the body needs these vitamins every day, foods containing them do not need to be eaten every day. The body will store unused fat-soluble vitamins in the liver and in fatty tissue and if high amounts are stored, it can be harmful.
- The water-soluble vitamins are vitamins B and C. They are found mainly in fruit, vegetables and grains. They can be destroyed by being exposed to heat or air and can be lost in the water used for cooking. Water-soluble vitamins are not stored in the body. Any excess of them is excreted. Therefore these vitamins need to be consumed daily to fulfil dietary requirements.

Table 2.4, on page 17, summarises the main functions and sources of vitamins A, B group, C and D, and highlights the impact on health of deficiency and excess of each.

Nutrient	Functions	Sources	Deficiency	Excess
Vitamin A	• Promotes: - healthy eyesight - healthy skin - normal growth and development - healthy immune system • Has ***antioxidant*** properties, protecting cells from damage	**Animal (*retinol*)** • Cheese, eggs, oily fish, whole milk, fortified margarine, liver **Plant (*carotene*)** • Carrots, green leafy vegetables (e.g. broccoli, cabbage), orange-coloured fruits (e.g. apricots, nectarines)	• Leads to poor vision in dim light and eventually to night blindness	• Excess retinol can be toxic • During pregnancy, large amounts of vitamin A can harm the unborn baby, leading to miscarriage or stillbirth
Vitamin D	• Helps regulate the amount of calcium in the body (needed for keeping bones and teeth healthy)	• Oily fish, eggs, butter, meat, fortified foods (e.g. margarine, breakfast cereals) • Most vitamin D is obtained from sunlight on the skin	• In children, leads to skeletal deformity called ***rickets*** • In adults, leads to pain and bone weakness called ***osteomalacia***	• Large amounts of vitamin D can weaken bones
B group vitamins: Vitamin B_1	• Assists with the release of energy from food	• Fortified cereals • Meat	• Causes lethargy • Can restrict growth	Excess is rare
B group vitamins: Vitamin B_{12}	• Promotes healthy blood	• Fortified cereals • Milk • Eggs	• Can cause anaemia	Excess is rare
B group vitamins: Folate	• Is important during pregnancy to prevent neural tube defects in the baby (e.g. ***spina bifida***) • Needed for red cell production and to prevent anaemia	• White bread • Fortified cereals • Green leafy vegetables (e.g. broccoli, cabbage) • Pulses	• Can increase risk of anaemia • In pregnancy, may cause neural tube defects in the baby (e.g. spina bifida)	Excess is rare
Vitamin C	• Helps protect and keep cells healthy • Helps the body absorb iron from food • Promotes development of connective tissue • Is involved in wound healing • Has antioxidant properties, protecting cells from damage	• Peppers • Broccoli • Sweet potato • Oranges • Kiwi fruit	• Leads to bleeding gums • Can prevent wounds from healing well	Excess is rare

Table 2.4: The functions and sources of vitamins and the effects of having too little or too much of them in the diet

WATER

Human beings are unable to survive without water, as it makes up over half of our body mass. As a result, regular fluid intake is essential for the correct functioning of virtually all cells.

The main functions of water are that it:

- acts as a lubricant for joints and eyes
- assists reactions in the body, such as digestion
- is a component of blood, which transports oxygen and nutrients
- helps the body get rid of waste
- helps to regulate body temperature.

As well as drinking water, there are other valuable food sources of water, such as fruit, vegetables and milk, which should be consumed to meet daily fluid requirements.

ACTIVITY 6

a We are advised to drink approximately two litres of water per day. Outline three functions of water in the diet.

b Identify a range of foods which contain a high proportion of water and which could be included in the diet to help meet daily fluid requirements.

GUIDELINE DAILY AMOUNTS

On many food labels, in the nutrition information, you will find a column of Guideline Daily Amounts (GDAs). The last column of the table on the left, from a packet of cheese biscuits, lists Guideline Daily Amounts for adults.

NUTRITION INFORMATION			
Average Values	Per 100g	Per Biscuit	UK Guideline Daily Amounts Adults
ENERGY	2015 kJ / 481 kcal	87 kJ / 21 kcal	2000kcal
PROTEIN	12.1g	0.5g	45g
CARBOHYDRATE	57.4g	2.5g	230g
of which Sugars	6.8g	0.3g	90g
FAT	22.5g	1.0g	70g
of which Saturates	13.4g	0.6g	20g
FIBRE	2.7g	0.1g	24g
SODIUM	1.1g	0.1g	2.4g

You may also see Guideline Daily Amounts on the front of packets, like this:

Each 40g serving provides

Calories	Sugars	Fat	Saturates	Salt
73	0.1g	8g	3.7g	0.1g
4%	<1%	11%	19%	2%

of the Guideline Daily Amounts

You can find out more about GDA labelling from the extracts on page 19, which are from the websites of the British Nutrition Foundation and the Institute of Grocery Distribution.

ACTIVITY 7

a Collect an example of a front-of-pack nutrition label displaying Guideline Daily Amounts (GDAs).

b Outline the information provided on the label about GDAs.

c Explain how the information about GDAs should be used.

d Evaluate how useful this information is in helping you to make healthy dietary choices.

HEALTHY EATING | EDUCATION

Front of Pack Labelling

GDA values were developed by the Institute of Grocery Distribution (IGD), and are based on recommendations made by the Committee on Medical Aspects of Food Policy (COMA) and the Scientific Advisory Committee on Nutrition (SACN). GDAs are commonly presented on the nutrition panel on the back of packets, but now several manufacturers and some retailers are using GDAs as the basis for front-of-pack labelling.

An example of a front-of-pack nutrition label based on GDAs is presented here. The amount of calories, sugars, fat, saturates and salt is displayed together with the percentage of the GDA that is provided in one portion of the food product.

Each portion contains:

Calories	Sugars	Fat	Saturates	Salt
139	6.0g	3.6g	1.0g	0.2g
7%	7%	5%	5%	3%

of an adult's guideline daily amount

Source: www.nutrition.org.uk

Home | Industry Expertise | Products | Servic

What are the Guideline Daily Amounts?

Guideline Daily Amounts (GDAs) help consumers make sense of the nutrition information provided on food labels. ...

GDAs are guidelines for healthy adults and children about the approximate amount of calories, fat, saturated fat, carbohydrate, total sugars, protein, fibre, salt and sodium required for a healthy diet.

Because people vary in many ways, such as size and activity levels, GDAs cannot be used as targets for individuals. ...

It is very difficult, if not impossible, for an individual to achieve the GDAs for all nutrients in any one day. ... The aim is to provide a guide for consumers to assist them in making appropriate dietary choices. For example, they can use them as a basis against which to judge the contribution of fat made by a particular food product to their diet.

Source: www.igd.com

Strategies for learning

There is a lot of information in this chapter which must be learned and applied to all aspects of Diet and Health. The following strategies can help with learning and applying your knowledge accurately. Some strategies will suit you better than others – so you decide which ones to use.

- ☐ Read, cover, remember
- ☐ Produce mind maps
- ☐ Produce question and answer cards
- ☐ Practise past exam paper questions
- ☐ Develop note-making grids
- ☐ Design a test paper and mark scheme
- ☐ Highlight notes using colour

Chapter 3

What's on the label?

Section A: Diet and Health

In this chapter you will learn about food labels. After studying the chapter, you should be able to analyse and use:

- nutrition panels
- lists of ingredients
- claims on labels
- dates on labels
- special dietary advice: vegetarian, allergy
- front-of-pack labelling systems.

Food labels are important sources of information, which can help consumers to make safer, healthier and better-informed choices when they are deciding which products to purchase. Food labelling is strictly governed by law. The Food Labelling Regulations (Northern Ireland) 1996 say that the following information must be clearly displayed on food packaging:

- the name of the food
- a list of ingredients
- a 'best before' or 'use by' date
- any special storage conditions or conditions of use
- the name and address of the manufacturer or packer, or of a seller established within the European Union (EU)
- the weight of the food.

Weight

The actual weight of the food, not including the packaging, must be stated.

Ingredients

Rice, Wheat (Wholewheat, Wheat Flour), Sugar, Wheat Gluten, Defatted Wheatgerm, Dried Skimmed Milk, Salt, Barley Malt Flavouring, Vitamin C, Niacin, Iron, Vitamin B_6, Riboflavin (B_2), Thiamin (B_1), Folic Acid, Vitamin D, Vitamin B_{12}.

Allergy Information

Contains: Milk, Wheat and Barley.

Ingredients

Ingredients used in the product are listed in descending order. This means that the main ingredients are listed first. Any ***additives*** (for example, flavourings) that are used must be included.

QUALITY CODES
BEST BEFORE
09/12/09
07 10:01
WX

'Best before' dates

These are put on foods that would be expected to be fit to eat and retain their quality for more than 18 months. This includes a wide range of frozen, dried and tinned foods.

'Best before' dates are more about quality than safety. After its 'best before' date, the food does not become harmful, but might begin to lose its flavour and texture. Responsible consumers should think carefully before throwing away food that is past its 'best before' date. They might be wasting food unnecessarily.

The 'best before' date is only accurate if the food is stored according to the instructions on the label, such as 'store in a cool dry place' or 'keep in the fridge once opened'.

'Use by' dates

Food manufacturers must state a 'use by' date on products that are highly perishable or go off quickly, such as meat products and ready prepared salads. This is the date by which the food should be eaten.

Food or drink should not be consumed after the end of the 'use by' date, even if it looks and smells fine. Using it after this date could be a risk to health.

It is vital to follow storage instructions on foods with a 'use by' date, such as 'keep in a refrigerator'. If these instructions are not followed, the food will spoil more quickly and the risk of food poisoning will increase.

Display until

Date marks such as 'display until' or 'sell by' often appear near or next to the 'best before' or 'use by' date. They are used by some shops to help with stock control. They are instructions for shop staff, not shoppers.

The Kellogg's Guarantee: *Kellogg's* is committed to providing quality products, and we welcome your comments and enquiries:

In the event of a complaint, please return the packet and its contents to:
(UK) Kellogg's Consumer Services Dept., P.O. Box 356, Warrington WA4 6XY.
(ROI) Kellogg's Consumer Services Dept., P.O. Box 1156, Crumlin, Dublin 12.
When you write please quote the quality codes on the top flap.

For any comments and enquiries you can contact us online:
(UK) www.kelloggsconsumercare.co.uk
(ROI) www.kelloggsconsumercare.ie
or telephone us on:
(UK) 0800 626066 or (ROI) 1800 626066
The Kellogg Care Lines are open from 8am to 6pm Monday to Friday.

Place of manufacture

The name and address of the manufacturer, packager or seller in the EU must appear on the label.

Special storage conditions or conditions of use

Instructions on food labels should be carefully followed to ensure that food can be enjoyed at its best. Examples of special instructions commonly found on food labels are 'freeze on day of purchase', 'cook from frozen', 'defrost thoroughly before use and use within 24 hours', 'store in a dry place' and 'keep in the fridge once opened'.

Nutrition information

Manufacturers must include nutrition information on food labels if they are making a nutritional claim about the product, such as 'low fat', 'low sugar' or 'high in fibre'. Increasingly, manufacturers are putting nutrition information on labels even when they are not making a claim about the product. They believe that keeping consumers well informed about their products will make them more inclined to purchase the brand.

Consumers need to be aware that some claims make the product sound healthy when, in fact, it isn't. For example, '93 per cent fat free' might sound low in fat, when it really means '7 per cent fat'!

The nutrition information on a label must show the amount of each of the following in 100 g or 100 ml of the food:

- energy (in kJ and kcal)
- protein (in g)
- carbohydrate (in g)
- fat (in g)

Information must also be given on the amount of any nutrient for which a claim has been made.

Sometimes amounts per serving are detailed, but this must be in addition to the 100 g or 100 ml breakdown.

Nutrition Information

	Typical value per 100 g		30 g serving with 125 ml of semi-skimmed milk	
ENERGY	1586 kJ	374 kcal	727 kJ*	171 kcal
PROTEIN	15 g		9 g	
CARBOHYDRATE	75 g		28 g	
of which are sugars	17 g		11 g	
starch	58 g		17 g	
FAT	1.5 g		2.5 g*	
of which saturates	0.5 g		1.5 g	
FIBRE	2.5 g		0.8 g	
SODIUM	0.45 g		0.2 g	
SALT	1.15 g		0.5 g	
VITAMINS:		(% RDA)		(% RDA)
VITAMIN D	8.3 µg	(167)	2.5 µg	(50)
VITAMIN C	100 mg	(167)	31 mg	(52)
THIAMIN (B_1)	2.3 mg	(167)	0.8 mg	(54)
RIBOFLAVIN (B_2)	2.7 mg	(167)	1.1 mg	(69)
NIACIN	30.1 mg	(167)	9.2 mg	(51)
VITAMIN B_6	3.3 mg	(167)	1.1 mg	(54)
FOLIC ACID	334 µg	(167)	108 µg	(54)
VITAMIN B_{12}	1.67 µg	(167)	1.02 µg	(102)
MINERALS:				
IRON	11.6 mg	(83)	3.5 mg	(25)

ACTIVITY 1

You have been commissioned by a local supermarket chain to design and produce a one-page flier telling shoppers how to make use of food labels. Use the information on these two pages to help you to write, design and produce the flier, using ICT.

TRAFFIC LIGHT LABELLING

A growing number of food manufacturers and supermarkets are using traffic light colours on food labels. 'Traffic lights' on the front of a pack show at a glance if the food has high, medium or low amounts of fat, saturated fat, sugars and salt.

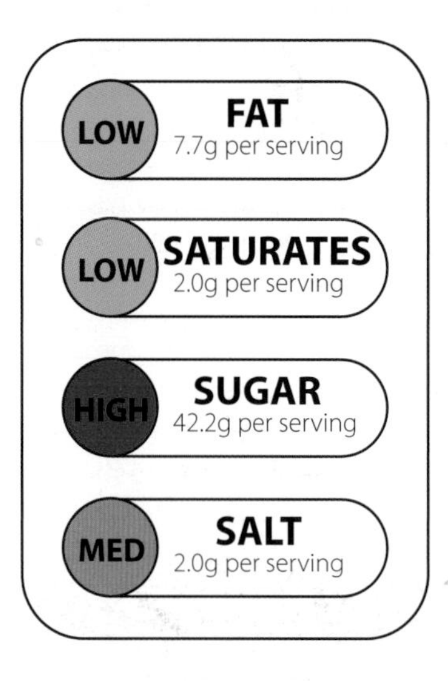

These are two versions of the traffic light labels used on food packaging.

It isn't always easy for consumers to make healthy choices about food. Traffic lights help. By choosing foods with as many greens as possible and avoiding too many reds, they will know that they are making a healthier choice.

Food manufacturers present traffic light labels on their labels in slightly different ways, but they all follow some design guidelines given by the Food Standards Agency. This ensures that consumers can easily recognise the colours when deciding on a purchase or comparing similar products in the supermarket.

The Food Standards Agency recommends that traffic light colours are used on ***convenience foods*** such as ready meals, pizzas, sausages, burgers, pies, sandwiches and breakfast cereals.

The British Heart Foundation designed this card about traffic light labelling, for people to keep in their purses or wallets. It provides information to help consumers make healthy choices when interpreting food labels.

PUT A TRAFFIC LIGHT ON EVERY FOOD LABEL

Traffic light labels on foods make it easier to choose healthy options.

Some supermarkets are using labels with % Guideline Daily Amounts (GDAs) instead.

To apply traffic lights to a product, look at the 'per 100g' information panel on the pack and use this grid to make a healthier choice.

All measures per 100g	Low – a healthier choice	Medium – ok most of the time	High – just occasionally
Sugars	5g or less	5.1g - 15g	More than 15g
Fat	3g or less	3.1 – 20g	More than 20g
Saturates	1.5g or less	1.6g - 5g	More than 5g
Salt	0.30g or less	0.31g - 1.5g	More than 1.5g

Ready Meals

Use this guide if there aren't any helpful traffic light colours on your ready meal. Levels will always be **high** if they are shown as:

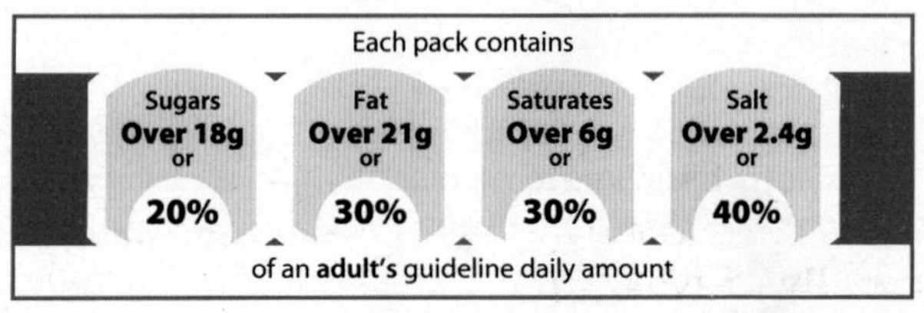

If you do choose a red product, why not balance it with some healthier options?

Join our campaign to get traffic lights on all food labels.

bhf.org.uk/campaigns

What do the traffic light colours mean?

A red light means that the food is high in one of the nutrients that we should be cutting down on. These foods should be used as treats and eaten in smaller amounts.

An amber light means that the food is neither high nor low in the nutrient and is a suitable choice most of the time.

A green light means that the food is low in the nutrient. The more green lights, the healthier the choice.

Many foods with this type of labelling have a mixture of colours. In order to make healthier choices, consumers should aim to choose more greens and ambers and fewer reds.

ACTIVITY 2

a Collect food labels from a range of food products, for example, breakfast cereals or ready meals, and record the fat, sugar and salt content per 100 g of each product.

b Using the information on the British Heart Foundation 'Put a Traffic Light on Every Food Label' card on page 22, allocate the appropriate traffic lights to each product.

c Evaluate the products and then make a final recommendation on the healthiest option, giving reasons for your choice.

SPECIAL DIETARY ADVICE

Some food packaging contains special dietary advice, such as information about whether the product is suitable for vegetarians or for people with certain allergies.

Vegetarian

If a food is labelled 'vegetarian', it usually means that the food doesn't contain any meat or animal products. As there is no single legal definition of the word 'vegetarian', there are no set rules about when a food can be called vegetarian. General labelling laws prohibit manufacturers and retailers from describing a food in a misleading way. However, what a 'vegetarian' food does or does not contain could vary from product to product. For strict vegetarians who want to avoid a particular ingredient, it is important to check the ingredients list on the food label.

Foods approved by the Vegetarian Society can display the society's 'seedling symbol' (see right). To be approved, the food must meet a number of conditions, not just be free of meat and animal-derived additives. For example, foods containing eggs will only be approved if the eggs used are free-range.

The shape in the centre of the Vegetarian Society logo is a symbol of a seedling, and also looks like a 'V'.

Allergies

People can be allergic to a wide variety of foods, and anyone with a specific food allergy should always read food labels carefully to avoid eating something that would have a negative impact on their health. It is particularly important for labels to say if a product includes nuts. Refer to Chapter 6 (pages 62–64) for more information on food allergies.

ACTIVITY 3

Find out which ingredients must be clearly shown on the labels of all pre-packed food sold in the UK to inform consumers and reduce the risk of an allergic reaction. The Food Standards Agency website (www.food.gov.uk) would be a good starting point for your research.

Chapter 4

Ages and stages

Section A: Diet and Health

In this chapter you will learn about the nutritional needs of people at the following stages of the lifespan:
- pre-conception and pregnancy
- baby/toddler (0–3 years)
- child (4–11years)
- adolescent (12–18 years)
- adults (19–64 years)
- older adults (65+ years)

After studying this chapter, you should be able to:
- discuss the relevant nutrients required for optimal health at each age and stage
- plan, make and evaluate meals and menus and modify recipes to meet the dietary needs of each age and stage.

At each stage of the lifespan a range of nutrients are required to achieve optimal health. While all nutrients are needed at each stage, the importance of each one varies depending on a number of factors. These include: stage of the lifespan, the person's level of physical activity and their state of health. When planning meals, it is important to remember that each lifespan stage has different nutritional requirements.

The nutrients we will be discussing in this chapter are:
- fat
- carbohydrate, including non-starch polysaccharide (NSP)
- protein
- minerals (calcium, iron, sodium)
- vitamins (A, D, B group, C)
- water.

PRE-CONCEPTION

A woman's health and ***nutritional status*** before she becomes pregnant are now known to affect her health, and the health of the fetus, during pregnancy. Women who are planning to get pregnant are advised to eat a balanced diet, with a variety of foods from the five food groups. It is important to be in optimal health at this stage, because any borderline deficiencies may worsen when the woman becomes pregnant. For example, a woman with low iron intake before conception is more likely to develop iron deficiency anaemia during pregnancy. It is also important to maintain a healthy weight before and during pregnancy.

PREGNANCY

Pregnant women need to make sure that their diet is providing enough energy and nutrients for their baby to grow and develop, and for their own body to cope with the changes taking place. Pregnancy is divided into three three-month periods, called trimesters, and nutrient demands increase most rapidly in the last trimester (months 7–9 of pregnancy). This is when the final growth and development of the fetus take place. However, it is untrue that a pregnant woman needs to 'eat for two'. She needs only an extra 200 kilocalories per day to meet her increased energy requirements.

Table 4.1 on pages 25–26 highlights the main nutritional needs during pregnancy.

Table 4.1: Nutritional needs during pregnancy

Nutrient	Requirements	Suitable foods
Fat	• Fat intake should be maintained rather than increased. Essential fatty acids play an important role in reducing high blood pressure in the mother and in the development of the brain/eye in the fetus.	Olive oil, oily fish (e.g. salmon), margarine and oatcakes
Carbohydrate	• Increased energy needs should be met by eating complex carbohydrates, which release energy slowly and provide a feeling of fullness. • Constipation can be a problem during pregnancy, so a diet high in NSP is recommended.	Bread, pasta, rice and potatoes Fruit, vegetables, wholegrain bread, pasta, cereals and rice
Protein	• More protein is needed for growth of the fetus and for repair and maintenance of the mother's body tissue during and after pregnancy.	Meat, fish, well-cooked eggs, milk, hard cheeses, pulses and cereals
Calcium	• The fetus requires a lot of calcium in the last trimester of pregnancy as the skeleton develops. • During pregnancy absorption of calcium from food increases to meet this increased need. • If the mother's diet was low in calcium before conception, she may lose calcium from her skeleton, which can cause her to have weakened bones and teeth.	Milk, hard cheeses, yogurt, fromage frais, fortified white bread and breakfast cereals
Iron	• The mother must have enough iron to meet her own needs and to provide her baby with a store of iron for the first months after birth. The baby will need this store for energy and healthy blood, as both breast milk and cows' milk (the baby's first food) are poor sources of iron. • As menstruation stops during pregnancy, and absorption of iron from food increases, the mother must meet her iron needs by a regular intake of iron-rich foods.	Meat, green leafy vegetables and fortified breakfast cereals
Sodium	• Sodium intake should be monitored to maintain steady blood pressure. Daily intake should not exceed 6 g.	Fruit, vegetables and pulses Avoid convenience, fast and processed foods
Vitamin A	• Necessary for growth and eye development of the fetus. • However, Vitamin A can be toxic in large amounts and can lead to birth defects.	Cheese, well-cooked eggs, oily fish, whole milk, fortified margarine, green leafy vegetables and orange-coloured fruits Avoid liver and liver products during pregnancy, as they are high in vitamin A
Vitamin D	• A deficiency can lead to low birth weight of the baby and to osteomalacia in the mother. • Assists the absorption of calcium.	Oily fish, well-cooked eggs, fortified margarine, milk and dairy products

Table continues on page 26

Table 4.1 continued: Nutritional needs during pregnancy

Nutrient	Requirements	Suitable foods
B group vitamins	• Folate is required for development of the brain and nervous system in the fetus. A lack of folate may lead to spina bifida, miscarriage, premature birth or slow growth.	White bread, fortified cereals, green leafy vegetables and pulses
	• A vegetarian mother may be deficient in vitamin B_{12} and may need to supplement her diet during pregnancy. The fetus stores vitamin B_{12} so that it has enough for the first six months after birth.	Fortified cereals Milk and eggs if not following a vegan diet
	• Vitamin B_1 helps the release of energy from nutrients in every cell in the body and helps meet increased energy needs in the final trimester of pregnancy (months 7–9).	Fortified cereals, milk, dairy products, meat, well-cooked eggs and green leafy vegetables
Vitamin C	• Assists the absorption of iron from food. • Helps improve immunity and prevent infections and disease. • Requirements increase in the last trimester (months 7–9) of pregnancy.	Fruit and vegetables
Water	• Fluid balance is important during pregnancy to prevent constipation and ***dehydration***. • A pregnant woman should aim to drink eight glasses of fluid a day.	Fruit and vegetables, water, soups, smoothies and pure fruit juices

Meal Planning during pregnancy

1 Follow the advice on the 'eatwell plate'.

2 Eat regular meals and include healthy snacks to maintain a healthy weight.

3 Avoid high-risk foods.

4 Maintain high standards of food hygiene to reduce the risk of food poisoning.

5 Eat wholegrain breads and cereals, as they contain NSP and folate.

ACTIVITY 1

a 'Eating for two' is a common misunderstanding about a woman's dietary needs during pregnancy. Discuss the nutrients required to maximise health at this stage of life.

b Outline a range of factors that should be considered when planning meals during pregnancy.

ACTIVITY 2

You are on work experience with a dietitian at a local hospital. The dietitian is currently working on advice to give to pregnant women on how to plan healthy meals. Using the information on pages 24–27, produce a resource that will promote a healthy diet during pregnancy.

Dietary advice for pregnancy

Every pregnant woman should follow this advice to ensure that her baby gets everything it needs and so that she has a healthy pregnancy.

Healthy diet, healthy baby!

Avoid these foods

- X Mould-ripened cheeses, e.g. Brie and Camembert
- X *Unpasteurised* cheese, for example, Stilton
- X Pâté
- X Pre-packed salads
- X 'Cook chill' meals

These foods may contain listeria bacteria, which can increase the risk of miscarriage or stillbirth.

- X Raw and lightly cooked eggs
- X Foods containing them (for example, mayonnaise)

These can contain salmonella which can cause food poisoning.

- X Raw and partly cooked meat
- X Unpasteurised milk
- X Unwashed fruit and vegetables

These foods could infect the body with toxoplasmosis, which can cause flu-like symptoms in the mother and damage the nervous system and eyes of the fetus.

- X Liver
- X Products made from liver (for example, pâté)

These foods contain high levels of vitamin A which can be toxic in excess, causing birth defects.

Limit intake of ...

Some types of fish

Pregnant women should aim to eat two portions of fish a week (one of which should be oily). Most types can be eaten, but some (for example, swordfish and tuna) should be restricted as they may contain mercury, which can affect the nervous system of the fetus.

Caffeine

Tea, coffee and soft drinks containing caffeine affect the absorption of many nutrients. Pregnant women are advised to have no more than 300 mg of caffeine per day. This would mean, for example, four cups of coffee, or six cups of tea, or eight cans of cola.

Alcohol

The Department of Health advises pregnant women not to drink more than one or two units of alcohol once or twice a week. Examples of one unit of alcohol are: one small glass of wine, half a pint of beer, or one single measure of spirits. There is evidence linking excess alcohol consumption during pregnancy to lower birth weights and miscarriage. Many experts advise no alcohol at all during pregnancy.

Use of supplements

Most supplements do not adequately provide the nutrients available from food, so they should not be used to replace a balanced diet. Also, supplements are often sold as megadoses, which makes it hard to know how much of each nutrient the body is absorbing. Some vitamins, for example, vitamin A, can be toxic in large amounts.

However, doctors DO advise women to take folic acid supplements. When trying to conceive and in the first twelve weeks of pregnancy, they should take 400 mcg of folic acid per day, in addition to the folate in their diet. This is advised partly because folate intake can be variable if the woman is eating a lot of processed food. Also, taking folic acid supplements reduces the risk of neural tube defects, such as spina bifida, in the fetus.

Lactation

A new mother's body produces milk for breastfeeding, in a process called ***lactation***. During lactation her body's energy needs and its demand for particular nutrients intensify. She needs to increase her intake of protein, calcium, vitamin D and fluid, to help produce milk. Women are advised to eat an extra portion of dairy products at this time, for example, milk on breakfast cereal, or yogurt with fruit as a midday snack.

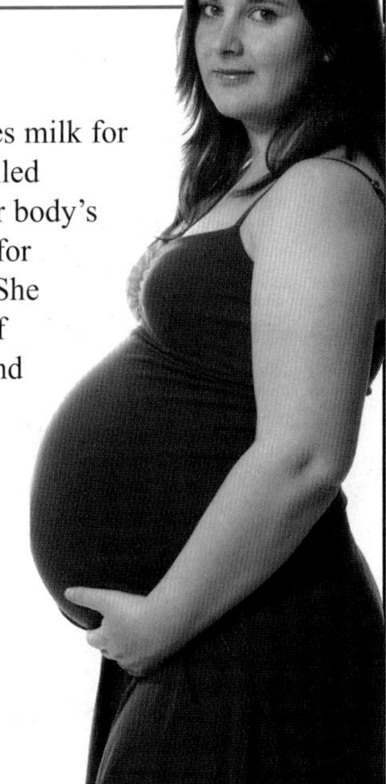

BABIES AND TODDLERS (0–3 YEARS)

Table 4.2 highlights the main nutritional needs of 0–3 year olds.

Table 4.2: The nutritional needs of babies and toddlers (ages 0–3 years)

Nutrient	Requirements	Suitable foods
Fat	• Whole milk and dairy products should be consumed to meet energy requirements, which are proportionately high at this stage because babies are growing rapidly and toddlers are active.	Whole milk, dairy products and lean meat
Carbohydrate	• Small portions of complex carbohydrates should be introduced. • Too much NSP should be avoided at this stage as it is very bulky and difficult to digest. This may suppress the baby's/toddler's appetite, so that they are unable to eat enough food to meet their nutritional needs. • Wholegrain foods should be limited as they can be bulky and difficult to digest at this stage.	White bread, pasta, rice, cereals, potatoes, fruit and vegetables
Protein	• Requirements increase moderately throughout this stage to help growth occur.	Meat, fish, eggs, milk and cheese
Calcium	• Required for healthy tooth and bone development.	Fortified white bread, milk and dairy products
Iron	• After six months iron stores are depleted and the diet must fulfil requirements.	Meat and meat products, green leafy vegetables and dried fruit
Sodium	• High intake of sodium can result in the baby/toddler becoming very ill as the kidneys are not fully developed.	Fresh home-made food Avoid processed foods, which are often high in hidden salt
Vitamin A	• Needed for healthy skin and brain development during this period of rapid growth.	Fruit, vegetables, whole milk and well-cooked eggs
Vitamin D	• Assists the absorption of calcium to help bones and teeth develop.	Egg yolk, fortified margarine, milk and dairy products
B group vitamins	• Vitamin B_1 helps with the release of energy required for this time of rapid growth and activity.	Fortified cereals and meat
Vitamin C	• Assists the absorption of iron from food. • Also helps improve immunity, and prevents infections common at this stage of development.	Fruit, vegetables and pure fruit juices
Water	• Fluid intake is important at this stage to maintain body temperature and prevent constipation.	Milk and water Avoid fizzy drinks and check drink labels for those with hidden sugar

Early feeding

Babies should be breastfed or fed with infant formula milk until they are six months old. Advantages of breastfeeding include benefits to health such as:

- antibodies to boost the baby's immune system and fight infection
- a supply of essential fatty acids which assist with brain development
- reduced likelihood of eczema, nappy rash, weight gain and constipation in baby
- increased protection against food-borne illness.

This six-month old is being weaned onto solid foods.

Mothers who do not breastfeed must ensure that only special infant formula milk is given to their baby. It is vital to follow the manufacturer's instructions, for the baby's well-being.

As babies grow, they have an increased need for energy, vitamins and minerals, which cannot be met by a diet of milk alone. Therefore, after six months, a mixed diet of liquid and solid foods should be introduced. This is called ***weaning***.

1 Young babies have not developed their chewing mechanism and have difficulty in swallowing and digesting lumps. When solid food is first introduced, it needs to be puréed and often diluted, for example, 'baby rice' mixed with baby milk and stewed fruit.

2 Once weaning is established, babies should be given harder foods, such as rusks or bread crusts, to encourage chewing.

3 Ensure a varied diet with a range of flavours and textures.

4 Never add salt to food given to babies and be aware of hidden salt in food.

5 At twelve months, whole cows' milk can be introduced as a drink. Whole milk provides more energy and vitamin A than semi-skimmed or skimmed milk.

ACTIVITY 3

a Discuss the nutritional requirements of toddlers and suggest a range of healthy foods that could be eaten to meet these needs.

b Plan a one-day menu suitable for a three-year old, presenting a range of reasons to justify your choice.

1 Plan meals that contain a wide range of nutrients and a variety of foods from the five food groups.

2 Consider how to make the food appealing, introducing a range of flavours, textures and colours to sustain the toddler's interest.

3 If using processed or convenience foods (even those designed for toddlers), read the labels carefully, as some of these foods can be high in hidden sugar and salt.

4 Try to encourage regular mealtimes and introduce healthy snacks (not too close to mealtimes).

5 Monitor treats and sugar intake as a 'sweet tooth' developed at this stage can contribute to dietary disorders later in the lifespan.

Toddlers who are faddy eaters

Some toddlers refuse to eat certain foods or want to avoid eating at all. This is common in early childhood and associated with growing up, asserting independence or seeking attention. While refusing food should not be encouraged, it is often a normal part of establishing eating patterns. Regular snacking and fluids should be maintained and good eating behaviour should be modelled by parents and other children. This can be a challenging time for parents and they should remember that no harm will come to their child by missing a meal. Creative and fun food, for example, pasta shapes, can be used to stimulate an interest in food.

ACTIVITY 4

Plan, make and evaluate a main meal dish that is suitable for a family with a toddler.

CHILDHOOD (4–11 YEARS)

This stage of the lifespan is one of the most diverse and it is important that dietary advice is taken in context. Energy requirements remain proportionately high, to meet the demands of growth and physical activity. Younger children will need small, frequent meals, which are energy-dense. Older children, with larger stomachs and increased appetites, can eat bulkier meals, while reducing the frequency of treats and snacks. At this stage of the lifespan it is important to introduce variety in the diet and to develop healthy eating patterns which can be carried on into adolescence and adulthood. Table 4.3, on page 32, highlights the main nutritional needs of 4–11 year olds.

Two dietary issues in this stage of the lifespan are described below.

School meal providers base their menus on the advice of the 'eatwell plate'.

Avoiding tooth decay

It is important to establish a good dental health routine in childhood, as this will have a positive effect on dental health throughout the lifespan. The frequency and volume of sugary foods eaten should be carefully monitored, and drinks should be limited to milk, water and unsweetened fruit juices. After teeth have been brushed, only water should be consumed.

Childhood obesity

Evidence suggests that, compared with in the past, some children are becoming less active. They spend more time watching television or playing computer games, rather than taking part in physical activity. Also, lifestyles have changed, with many people relying on a car or public transport rather than walking. Alongside this, our appetite for foods high in fat and sugar has increased, and ***fast food*** consumption and '***grazing***' eating patterns have intensified. Over time this can lead to obesity, as energy intake from food exceeds the amount of energy the body uses. The extra energy is converted into fat and stored in the body. The best way to reduce the risk of childhood obesity is to eat a balanced diet and take regular physical activity.

Table 4.3: The nutritional needs of children (ages 4–11 years)

Nutrient	Requirements	Suitable foods
Fat	• Essential fatty acids are important for brain development. • Fat should not be more than 35 per cent of total energy (kcal) intake.	Semi-skimmed milk, oily fish, dairy products and lean meat
Carbohydrate	• Complex carbohydrates should be the main source of energy, as they are filling but low in calories. • Consumption of non-milk extrinsic sugars (NMES) should be reduced and should not exceed 10 per cent of total energy intake. • NSP-rich foods should be consumed to reduce the risk of constipation.	Wholegrain cereals, wholegrain bread, pasta, rice, potatoes, fruit and vegetables
Protein	• Requirements increase to facilitate growth and repair.	Meat, fish, eggs, milk and cheese
Calcium	• Required for healthy tooth and bone development.	Fortified white bread, milk and dairy products
Iron	• Needed to prevent iron deficiency anaemia, which is common in childhood. • Faddy eaters or children following a vegetarian diet could be particularly at risk.	Meat and meat products, green leafy vegetables, fortified breakfast cereals and dried fruit
Sodium	• Excess sodium should be avoided to reduce impact on the kidneys. • Intake of salt should not exceed 3 g per day.	Fresh home-made food, fruit and vegetables Avoid processed foods, which are often high in hidden salt
Vitamin A	• Needed for healthy skin and brain development.	Fruit, vegetables, milk and dairy products
Vitamin D	• Assists the absorption of calcium to help bones and teeth develop.	Egg yolk, oily fish, fortified margarine, milk and dairy products
B group vitamins	• Vitamin B_1 helps with the release of energy required for this time of rapid growth and activity. • A vegetarian child may be deficient in vitamin B_{12}.	Fortified cereals and meat Fortified cereals, milk and eggs, if not following a vegan diet
Vitamin C	• Assists the absorption of iron from food. • Also helps improve immunity, and prevents infections common at this stage of development.	Fruit, vegetables and pure fruit juices
Water	• Fluid intake is important at this stage to maintain body temperature and prevent constipation.	Milk and water Avoid fizzy drinks and check drink labels for hidden sugar

Meal Planning for children

1 Prepare three meals a day, which contain a variety of foods and provide a range of nutrients. Follow the advice on the 'eatwell plate'.

2 Make eating enjoyable. Parents should model good eating behaviour. When possible, eat meals as a family, to establish good eating habits.

3 Supplement meals with healthy snacks, such as fruit, rather than with snacks high in salt, sugar and fat, such as crisps, sweets and fizzy drinks.

4 Involve children when preparing and serving meals, to encourage a lifelong interest in food and healthy eating.

5 Encourage children to have a healthy breakfast, which should meet 25 per cent of their daily energy needs.

ACTIVITY 5

Plan, make and evaluate a school packed lunch for a six-year old child. Explain how the lunch would contribute to the child's nutritional requirements.

ADOLESCENCE (12–18 YEARS)

During adolescence teenagers experience an increase in their rate of growth (height and weight). This is called the 'adolescent growth spurt'. A girl's growth spurt starts at approximately 10 to 11 years of age and a boy's at around 12 to 13 years of age. The onset of this development can account for many nutritional differences at this stage of the lifespan.

A balanced diet during adolescence is important for supporting growth and preventing diet-related disorders that can continue into adulthood.

Table 4.4 on page 34 highlights the main nutritional needs of adolescents. On the right and on page 35 are some dietary issues that are especially important to think about in this stage of the lifespan.

Teen Talk

Special diets

In adolescence young people become more independent about their food choices and also more susceptible to peer pressure. This can make it more difficult for those who have a food allergy to manage it.

Sport

Many teenagers take part in sporting activities and they will need more energy-dense foods.

Images in the media can lead young people to feel negative about their own body – for example, thinking they are too fat. A balanced diet and regular exercise are essential and slimming diets should be treated with caution.

Many adolescents, particularly girls, choose to become vegetarians. They should make sure that they supplement their diet with a variety of foods that supply the nutrients they will be missing by not eating meat or animal products.

Table 4.4: The nutritional needs of adolescents (ages 12–18 years)

Nutrient	Requirements	Suitable foods
Fat	• Care is needed to meet increased energy requirements to help growth while also monitoring fat intake. • Fat should not provide more than 35 per cent of total energy (kcal) intake.	Milk, lean meat, semi-skimmed milk and low-fat dairy products
Carbohydrate	• Starchy carbohydrates rather than non-milk extrinsic sugars (NMES) should be eaten, as they are energy-dense rather than empty calories. • NSP-rich foods should be consumed to reduce the risk of constipation – 18 g of NSP per day is recommended.	Bread, pasta, rice, potatoes, fruit, vegetables and wholegrain cereals
Protein	• Required to help growth and repair of tissues. • Can be a secondary source of energy to meet demands of the growth spurt or high levels of physical activity. • Male adolescents have proportionately more muscle than females and so have higher protein requirements.	Meat, fish, chicken, pulses, nuts, seeds, milk and dairy products
Calcium	• Calcium is essential in adolescence to help achieve peak bone mass and reduce the risk of osteoporosis in later life.	Milk, yogurt, cheese and fortified cereals
Iron	• Iron is particularly important for adolescent girls to make up for iron loss through menstruation and to prevent iron deficiency anaemia.	Meat, green leafy vegetables, fortified cereals and dried fruit
Sodium	• Sodium intake should be no more than 6 g per day.	Fresh home-made food, fruit and vegetables Avoid processed foods, often high in hidden salt
Vitamin A	• During adolescence the skin can be affected by hormones and an unhealthy diet. Vitamin A can contribute to healthy skin.	Fruit, vegetables, fortified cereals and margarine
Vitamin D	• Assists absorption of calcium, to help bones and teeth develop and aid the development of peak bone mass.	Eggs, margarine, milk and dairy products
B group vitamins	• Vitamin B_1 helps with the release of energy required for this time of rapid growth and activity.	Meat, dairy products and fortified breakfast cereals
	• A vegetarian adolescent may be deficient in vitamin B_{12} and will need to eat fortified foods, dairy products and maybe supplements.	Fortified cereals, milk and eggs if not following a vegan diet
	• Folate requirements are high to prevent anaemia.	White bread, fortified cereals, green leafy vegetables, pulses
Vitamin C	• Assists absorption of iron, particularly important for adolescents who need to increase their iron intake to reduce the risk of iron deficiency anaemia. • Improves immunity and prevents infection and disease.	Fruit, vegetables and fruit juices
Water	• Drinking two litres of water a day will help to promote healthy skin.	Milk and water Reduce fizzy drinks and check drink labels for hidden sugar

Teen Talk

Fast food meals

Not all fast food can be labelled 'junk food', as some items can make a nutrient contribution. For example, a hamburger provides protein, fat-soluble vitamins and iron. However, this is often at a price, as it will be high in calories, sugar, saturated fat and salt.

Most fast food options are not balanced meals as they are low in vitamins, minerals and NSP.

The occasional fast food meal will not have any lasting impact on health, but regular consumption, combined with inactivity, is a major factor contributing to weight gain during adolescence.

Breakfast

Eating breakfast should provide:

- 25 per cent of daily energy and nutrients
- complex carbohydrate, protein, calcium, iron, B group vitamins, vitamin C and NSP
- a better ***metabolism***, which will help maintain a healthy weight.

Missing breakfast could lead to:

- grazing or snacking on foods high in fat and sugar but with limited nutritional value
- poor concentration, affecting ability to perform at school.

Meal Planning for adolescents

1 **Follow the advice from the 'eatwell plate'.**

2 **Follow the Food Standards Agency's '8 tips for eating well'.**

3 **Girls should ensure that their intake of iron is enough to avoid iron deficiency anaemia.**

4 **Adolescents should be encouraged to take an interest in planning and preparing meals, in order to extend their skills, promote independence and manage their own health.**

5 **Read food labels carefully and avoid over-reliance on convenience foods and ready meals, which can be high in fat, salt and sugar but low in NSP and other nutrients.**

ACTIVITY 6

a Plan, make and evaluate a range of meals that you could make quickly at home as a healthier alternative to fast food.

b Justify why the 'tip for eating well', 'Don't skip breakfast' is particularly important for adolescents.

ADULTHOOD (19–64 YEARS)

Adulthood is the longest stage of the lifespan and a time when people tend to take fitness and good health for granted. In reality this is an important time to maintain a healthy body, in order to meet the demands of the future. From the age of 30 the basal metabolic rate (BMR) begins to slow and it is important to monitor intake of high-density, low-nutrient foods, such as cakes and biscuits, and to maintain a healthy weight by taking regular exercise. Balancing energy intake and energy used reduces the likelihood of excess weight gain and the associated impact on health.

Table 4.5 (opposite) highlights the main nutritional needs of adults. The news cuttings on this page look at two dietary issues for adulthood.

Antioxidants

Vitamin A (carotene) and vitamin C have antioxidant properties. This means that they form part of the body's defence against dangerous substances called 'free radicals', which are linked to the development of some cancers and coronary heart disease.

Free radicals are produced naturally by the body and, under normal circumstances, the body's defence system is able to prevent them from causing tissue damage. However, as the risks of coronary heart disease and cancer become more common with age, adults are advised to keep up their intake of vitamins A and C, by eating at least five portions of fruit and vegetables every day.

Weight management

Adults should be conscious of the need to achieve energy balance and aim to maintain a body weight that is appropriate for their height. An increasing number of adults are ***overweight*** and obese.

A quick way to find out if an adult's weight could have a negative impact on health is to determine their ***body mass index*** (BMI). (For more information, see page 52.) A BMI of over 30 is obese.

It is not just a problem of excess weight. Where the weight is deposited matters too. 'Apple-shaped' people who have extra weight around their middle are at greater risk of some diet-related diseases, such as coronary heart disease and diabetes, than 'pear-shaped' adults whose extra weight is mostly around their hips and thighs.

Meal Planning for adults

1 **Follow the advice on the 'eatwell plate'.**

2 **Eat five portions of fruit and vegetables a day. Aim to eat a wide range of colourful options to add variety, *sensory appeal* and nutritional benefits.**

3 **Try to limit snacking and grazing during the day, for example, at work.**

4 **Read labels to identify foods containing high levels of saturated fat, salt and sugar and replace these with healthier options.**

5 **Try to sustain an interest in food by planning creative and interesting meals, for example, a recipe from a different country.**

ACTIVITY 7

a Plan, make and evaluate a creative and interesting two-course meal for a special occasion.

b Discuss a range of diet and lifestyle factors that adults should consider in order to maintain good health and prevent disease.

Table 4.5: The nutritional needs of adults (ages 19–64 years)

Nutrient	Requirements	Suitable foods
Fat	• Fat intake needs to be monitored. Too much saturated fat can contribute to obesity, coronary heart disease, hypertension and diabetes. • Essential fatty acids Omega 3 and Omega 6 are important due to their positive effect on blood cholesterol and blood pressure.	Milk, lean meat, olive oil and margarine Margarine, soya beans, green vegetables, oily fish and seafood
Carbohydrate	• Carbohydrate requirements should be met by eating complex starchy carbohydrates rather than non-milk extrinsic sugars (NMES). NMES are high in calories but provide a limited range of other nutrients. • Soluble NSP can help reduce blood cholesterol levels. It also helps control blood sugar levels. • Insoluble NSP helps to prevent constipation and provides a feeling of fullness, which can decrease the desire to eat between meals and therefore help to maintain a healthy weight.	Wholemeal bread, pasta, rice, potatoes, fruit, vegetables and wholegrain cereals
Protein	• Required for repair of tissues and recovery from illness.	Lean meat, milk, eggs and pulses
Calcium	• Peak bone mass is reached around the age of 35 and so calcium needs remain high, particularly for young adult women. • After this age calcium is required for the maintenance and repair of bones.	Milk, cheese, yogurt, fromage frais and fortified white bread
Iron	• Requirements remain high for adult females as they need to replace the iron lost by menstruation to prevent iron deficiency anaemia.	Meat, meat products, pulses and green leafy vegetables
Sodium	• High sodium consumption at this stage increases blood pressure and contributes to the development of hypertension, a risk factor for coronary heart disease. • Consumption should not exceed 6 g per day.	Avoid processed foods, often high in hidden salt Use herbs and spices to season food
Vitamin A	• Vitamin A is an antioxidant and is thought to protect against coronary heart disease and some cancers.	Fruit and vegetables
Vitamin D	• Assists the absorption of calcium.	Egg yolk, margarine, milk and dairy products
B group vitamins	• Intake should be maintained for general well-being.	Meat, dairy products, fortified bread and cereals
Vitamin C	• Is an antioxidant and is thought to protect against coronary heart disease and some cancers. • Assists the absorption of iron from food. • Improves immunity and prevents infection and disease.	Fruit, vegetables, and fruit juices
Water	• Fluid intake is necessary to prevent constipation. • Approximately two litres per day.	Milk, water, tea and coffee

OLDER ADULTS (65+YEARS)

The nutritional needs of older adults are generally similar to those of other adults. The main difference is that energy requirements decline due to a decrease in the basal metabolic rate and reduced levels of physical activity. However, it is important not to stereotype older adults. People are living longer, and many people in the 65+ age group remain active, with a healthy interest in food.

Table 4.6 on page 39 highlights the main nutritional needs of older adults. Some particular issues for this stage of the lifespan are discussed on this page.

Malnutrition

Malnutrition includes under-nutrition (not eating enough or not getting enough nutrients) and over-nutrition (eating too much and getting excess nutrients, usually fat, sugar and sodium). Older adults must remember the importance of balancing energy intake and energy use, to achieve a healthy weight. Being overweight or underweight can influence the onset of diet-related diseases such as diabetes and osteoporosis.

Appetite can decline with advancing age and a varied diet of smaller meals, supplemented with regular snacks, should be eaten.

Enjoyment of food

With advancing age, the senses of taste and smell may decline, and this can make food seem less appetising. Variety of taste, texture, colour and flavour is the key to sustaining an interest in food. Enjoyment of food can also be affected by isolation and economic factors. Many people say that they can't see the point of cooking for one. Sharing food with family and friends or taking part in local food-related events, for example, coffee mornings or day trips, can help people to engage with food again.

Use of supplements

As vitamin D is mainly obtained from the action of sunlight on the skin, older adults who are housebound or in long-term hospital care may be at risk of vitamin D deficiency. A vitamin D supplement of 10 mcg per day is recommended for everyone over 65.

Meal Planning for older adults

1 **Meals should be nutrient-dense rather than energy-dense.**

2 **Eat a variety of foods from the five food groups.**

3 **Reduce the size of meals and supplement with regular snacks.**

4 **Plan meals that are full of flavour. Use herbs and spices, rather than salt, to add flavour.**

5 **Aim to have a store cupboard of items that are versatile and nutritious, for example, tinned soup.**

ACTIVITY 8

a Design a range of recipe cards focusing on meals that are nutrient-dense and suitable for an older adult.

b Plan, make and evaluate one of the meals and explain how it meets the nutritional requirements of an older person.

Table 4.6: The nutritional needs of older adults (65+ years)

Nutrient	Requirements	Suitable foods
Fat	• Fat is important as a concentrated source of energy. • Saturated fats should be avoided as they increase cholesterol and the risk of coronary heart disease.	Oily fish, olive oil, nuts, seeds and margarine
Carbohydrate	• Carbohydrate needs should be met by consuming complex starchy carbohydrates rather than non-milk extrinsic sugars (NMES), which are high in calories but provide a limited range of other nutrients. • It is important that older adults still eat complex carbohydrates rich in NSP to avoid constipation and other bowel-related disorders common at this stage.	Wholegrain bread, cereals, pulses, fruit and vegetables
Protein	• Protein requirements may increase to help repair of tissues and recovery from illness.	Lean meat, milk, eggs and pulses
Calcium	• An adequate intake of calcium can help to slow age-related bone loss, which can result in osteoporosis.	Milk, dairy products, fortified white bread, green vegetables and canned fish (eaten with the bones)
Iron	• Iron absorption may be lower in older adults (this can be linked to medication) and iron deficiency anaemia is common at this stage of the lifespan. • Women's need for iron reduces after menstruation stops.	Meat, fortified cereals, bread, eggs, pulses, dried fruit and dark green leafy vegetables
Sodium	• Sodium intake should be cut down to reduce the risk of high blood pressure, stroke and coronary heart disease.	Avoid processed foods, often high in hidden salt Season food with herbs and spices
Vitamin A	• Intake should be maintained for continued protection against coronary heart disease and some cancers.	Fruit and vegetables
Vitamin D	• Vitamin D is needed for the absorption of calcium from food and for maintaining and repairing bones.	Oily fish, margarine, eggs and fortified cereals
B group vitamins	• Older men and women have less need for the B group vitamins, because of reduced energy requirements.	Fortified cereals, bread and green leafy vegetables
Vitamin C	• Vitamin C is an antioxidant, thought to offer protection against coronary heart disease and some cancers. • Assists the absorption of iron from food. • Improves immunity and prevents infection and disease.	Fruit, vegetables and fruit juices
Water	• Fluid intake is important at this stage to maintain body temperature and prevent constipation.	Tea, coffee, milk, soups, stews, fruit and vegetables

Chapter 5

Dietary disorders

In this chapter you will learn about a range of dietary disorders. After studying the chapter, you should be able to:

- discuss the diet and lifestyle factors that may contribute to the development of dietary disorders
- suggest and justify diet and lifestyle advice to manage dietary disorders
- identify the ages and stages most at risk from each of the dietary disorders
- plan, make and evaluate meals and menus and modify recipes to meet the dietary needs of individuals at risk from dietary disorders.

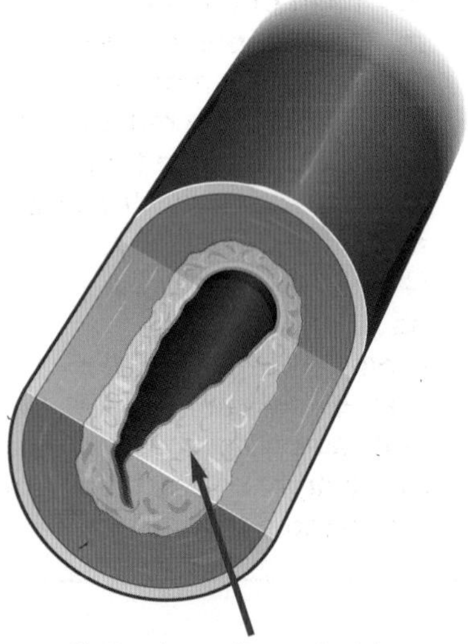

This cross-section drawing of a coronary artery shows how fatty deposits can build up on the artery walls. This narrows the inside of the artery.

CORONARY HEART DISEASE

The coronary arteries supply blood to the heart. Coronary heart disease can occur when one or more of the coronary arteries is narrowed, or completely blocked, by a build-up of fatty deposits on its walls. This is called ***atherosclerosis***. It restricts blood flow through the arteries and this causes damage to the heart muscle.

When the arteries become partly or totally blocked, the heart has to work much harder to pump blood around the body. If the arteries become totally blocked, blood cannot flow to the heart and this can result in a ***heart attack***.

There are several diet and lifestyle factors that increase a person's risk of developing coronary heart disease, as shown on page 41. Since the risk increases with age, adults and older people are more likely to develop the condition. Coronary heart disease can often be prevented and there are many things that people can do to help protect their heart and keep it healthy, whatever their age.

The importance of diet

A healthy, well-balanced diet reduces the risk of developing coronary heart disease because eating healthily helps to:

- maintain a healthy weight
- lower blood cholesterol levels
- keep blood pressure within safe limits
- prevent atherosclerosis.

ACTIVITY 1

Discuss the role of diet and lifestyle factors in the development of coronary heart disease.

High blood pressure, also known as hypertension, is a condition where the blood flows through the arteries at a constantly higher pressure than recommended. Having high blood pressure increases a person's risk of a heart attack or a stroke. It can cause the heart to become abnormally large, and the pumping action of the heart may become less effective.

High blood pressure may be caused by:

- physical inactivity
- being overweight
- a diet high in salt and low in fruit and vegetables
- high alcohol consumption.

Risk factors for coronary heart disease

Eating too much fat, particularly saturated fat, can increase blood cholesterol levels. High levels of cholesterol increase the risk of coronary heart disease.

Eating too much salt can increase blood pressure levels, and so increase the risk of developing coronary heart disease.

Being overweight increases a person's risk of developing several serious and possibly life-threatening medical conditions, including coronary heart disease and diabetes.

Too much alcohol can damage the heart muscle, cause an increase in blood pressure and lead to weight gain – all of which increase the risk of coronary heart disease.

Lack of physical activity means that the heart (which is a muscle) does not get the exercise it needs to ensure that it functions properly. Also, inactive people are more likely to be overweight.

Smoking almost doubles a person's risk of a heart attack. Smoking damages the lining of the arteries, so that fatty deposits build up there. Carbon monoxide in cigarette smoke reduces the amount of oxygen that the blood can carry to the heart and around the body. Nicotine in cigarettes stimulates the body to produce adrenaline, which makes the heart beat faster and raises blood pressure. Smoking may also make the blood more likely to clot.

A family history of coronary heart disease increases a person's risk of developing it. This cannot be changed, but people in this situation can do many things to lessen their risk: taking care with their diet, managing their weight, not smoking, not drinking too much alcohol and keeping up their levels of physical activity.

Diabetes increases the risk of coronary heart disease. (For more on diabetes, see page 44.) High blood sugar levels may affect the artery walls and increase the likelihood of high cholesterol levels and high blood pressure.

The role of diet in the development of coronary heart disease

This poster was designed by the British Nutrition Foundation to highlight the role of diet in the development of coronary heart disease.

ACTIVITY 2

Using the information on pages 40–41 and 43, create a poster highlighting the impact of lifestyle factors on the development of coronary heart disease.

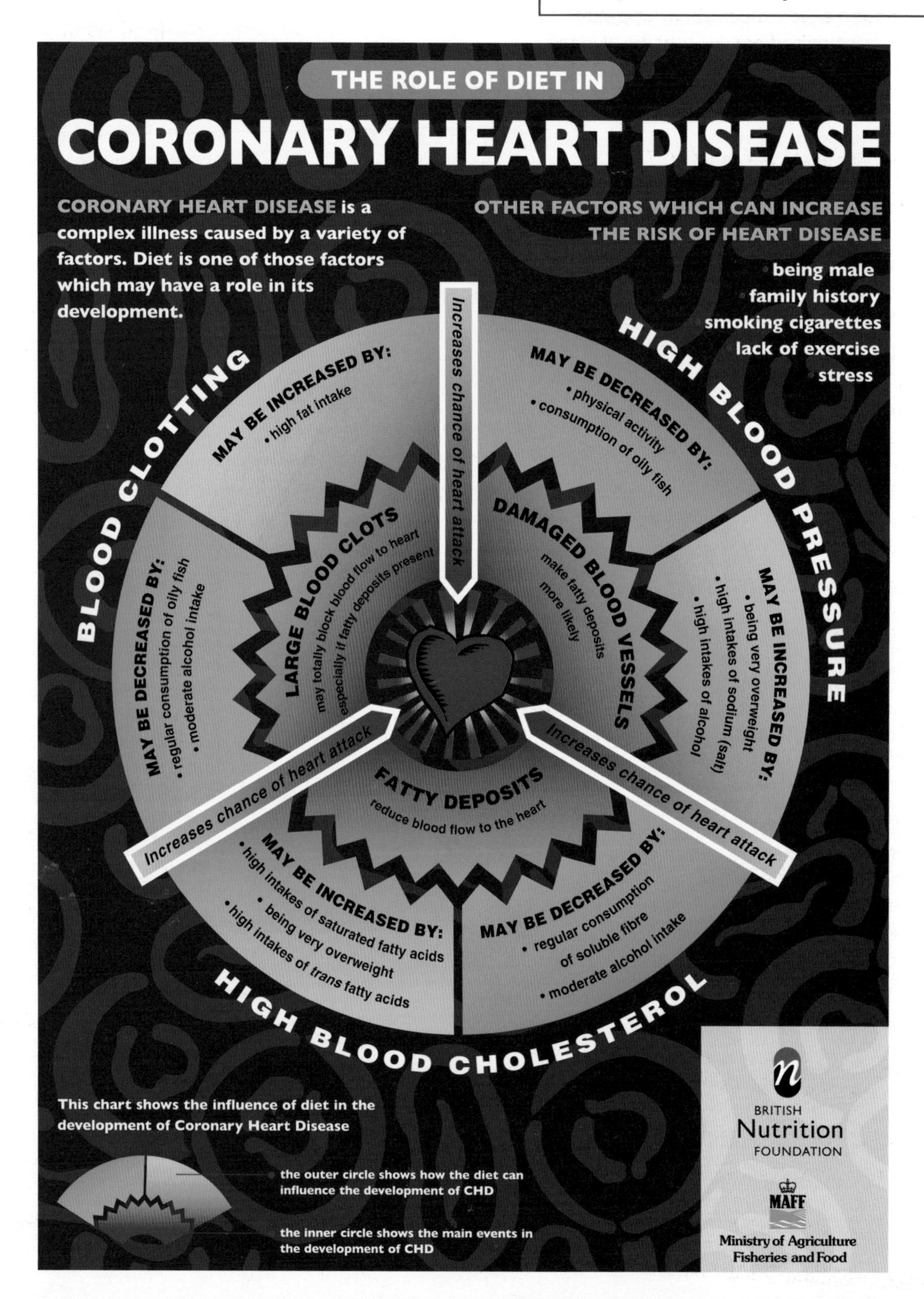

ACTIVITY 3

a Read the dietitian's case notes, below.
b Compile a 'Top Ten Tips', highlighting practical ways to reduce intake of saturated fat.
c Using the information in the case notes, produce a fact sheet about cholesterol for adults at risk of coronary heart disease.

ALMS General Hospital

Dietitian's Case Notes

Patient name: Mrs Eve Chapman

Date: 21.09.09

Dietary disorder: Coronary heart disease

Following consultation the following advice was given:

- Evidence suggests that a diet rich in fruit and vegetables can help lower the risk of coronary heart disease. Eat at least five portions of fresh, frozen, dried, tinned or juiced fruit and vegetables each day.
- To help reduce cholesterol levels, cut down on the total amount of fat eaten and replace saturated fats with unsaturated fats.
- Don't forget: all fat is high in calories. So limit total fat intake to maintain a healthy weight.
- Eat fish regularly: at least two portions a week, one of which should be oily. Eating oily fish such as salmon and tuna, which are rich in the essential fatty acid Omega 3, can help to protect against heart disease.
- Reduce the amount of salt you eat to help keep blood pressure down.
- Use vegetables, beans or pulses, instead of meat, in some dishes to reduce intake of saturated fat and to increase the amount of soluble NSP in the diet, which can help lower cholesterol.
- Find out about cholesterol and its impact on healthy hearts. Cholesterol is a fatty substance found in the blood and is mainly made in the body. Cholesterol plays an essential role in how every cell in the body works. However, too much cholesterol in the blood can increase the risk of heart problems. There are two types of cholesterol. Low-density lipoprotein (LDL) is a harmful type of cholesterol, and high-density lipoprotein (HDL) is a protective type of cholesterol. Having too much harmful cholesterol in the blood can increase the risk of coronary heart disease.
- Get active, as physical activity can help increase HDL cholesterol.
- Maintain safe blood pressure levels by being physically active, keeping a healthy weight, reducing salt and alcohol intake and eating more fruit and vegetables.
- Avoid smoking and seek advice about giving up if necessary.
- Reduce the risk of developing diabetes by controlling weight and regular physical activity. People with diabetes should aim to control blood sugar, blood pressure and cholesterol.

DIABETES

During digestion of food, the body produces ***glucose*** (sugar) and uses it for energy. A hormone called ***insulin*** helps the glucose to enter the cells and, as this happens, the level of glucose in the blood goes down.

Diabetes is a condition where the amount of glucose in the blood is too high. It develops either because the body does not produce insulin as needed, or because the insulin that it does produce does not work effectively. Both of these things lead to an abnormally high level of glucose in the blood.

The charity Diabetes UK estimates that there are currently over 2.5 million people with diabetes in the UK. It also estimates that more than half a million people in the UK have diabetes and do not know it.

There are two types of diabetes.

- In Type 1 diabetes, the body cannot make any insulin. Type 1 diabetes occurs more commonly in children, adolescents and young adults. It is also known as insulin dependent diabetes.
- In Type 2 diabetes, not enough insulin is produced, or the insulin produced in the body doesn't work effectively. Type 2 diabetes tends to develop gradually as people get older – usually after the age of 40. It is also known as non-insulin dependent diabetes.

Because Type 2 diabetes develops gradually, adults and older people are at greater risk of developing it. However, in recent years, the number of children and adolescents being identified with Type 2 diabetes has been rising, as children become less active and more overweight. The importance of preventing Type 2 diabetes in children cannot be overstated, as it is a progressive, lifelong condition that can lead to serious complications.

ACTIVITY 4

a Carry out research to determine the current statistics for people with diabetes, using, for example, www.diabetes.org.uk

b Write an attention-grabbing headline and newspaper report on your findings.

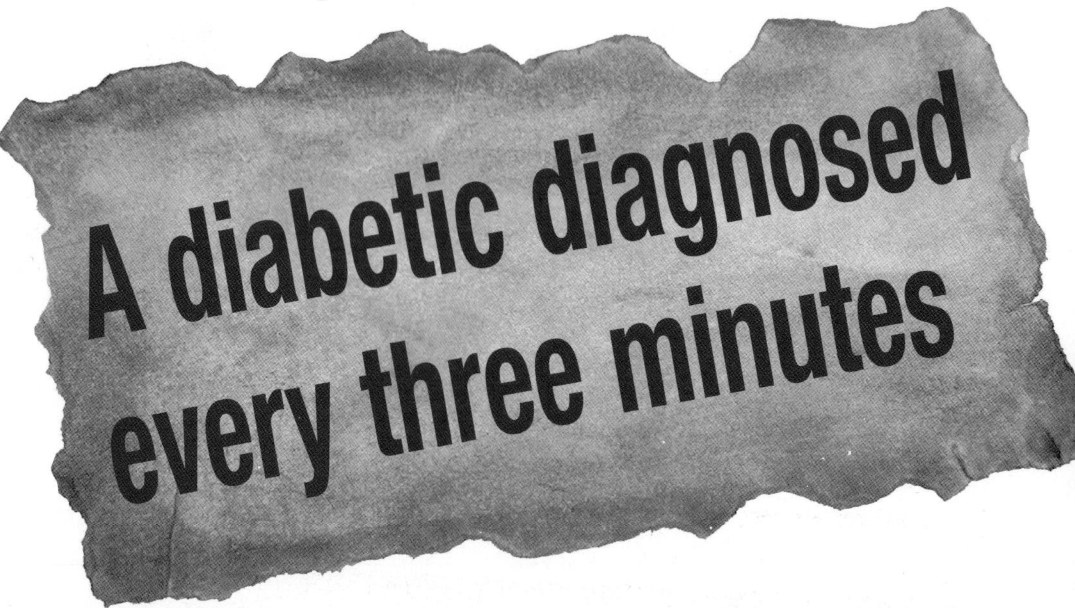

This headline appeared in the national press in January 2009, highlighting the growing concern about the increase in cases of Type 2 diabetes being diagnosed in the UK.

Risk factors for diabetes

Several diet and lifestyle factors increase people's risk of developing diabetes.

The cause of Type 1 diabetes is uncertain. It is thought that the insulin-producing cells in the body have been gradually destroyed and that this may have been triggered by a virus or other type of infection. People who have a relative with diabetes are more likely to develop the condition.

The risk factors for Type 2 diabetes are much clearer. Statistics show that over 80 per cent of people diagnosed with Type 2 diabetes are overweight. The more overweight and the more inactive you are, the greater your risk.

In 2009 Diabetes UK started a roadshow campaign to increase awareness of diabetes. The campaign highlights the link between a person's waist measurement and their risk of Type 2 diabetes.

Some of the risk factors for Type 2 diabetes

Age

The risk of developing Type 2 diabetes increases with age, so the older you get, the more at risk you are.

Being overweight or obese

The risk of developing Type 2 diabetes increases if you are overweight or if your waist measurement is:

- ✗ 31 1/2 inches or over for women
- ✗ 35 inches or over for Asian men
- ✗ 37 inches or over for white and black men.

Leading an inactive lifestyle

Being inactive can contribute to weight gain and increase your risk of developing Type 2 diabetes.

Family history

The risk of developing Type 2 diabetes increases if diabetes is in the family. The closer the relative is, for example, mother, father, brother or sister, the greater the risk.

Other health problems

If you have been diagnosed with any circulation problems, had a heart attack or stroke, or if you have high blood pressure, you may be at an increased risk of diabetes.

ACTIVITY 5

Design a web page giving advice on the prevention of Type 2 diabetes.

ACTIVITY 6

a Read this interview with a dietitian.

b Role-play a consultation between the dietitian and someone recently diagnosed with diabetes. As the dietitian, you will want to give practical advice on managing the condition. As the person with diabetes, you will need some questions to ask.

c Mrs Brown, aged 56, has been diagnosed with non-insulin dependent diabetes. Explain the differences between insulin dependent and non-insulin dependent diabetes.

d Discuss four factors that Mrs Brown should take into account when planning her diet.

A dietitian tells us about diabetes

What can you do for people with diabetes?

Diabetes cannot be cured, but it can be very successfully treated. I am involved daily with patients who have diabetes, some Type 1 and some Type 2. The main aim of treatment, for both types, is to achieve blood glucose, blood pressure and cholesterol levels that are as near to normal as possible. Together with a healthy lifestyle, this helps to improve well-being and protect against long-term damage.

What advice do you give about diet?

It's exactly the same as for everyone! Eat a healthy, balanced diet, low in fat, sugar and salt, and including plenty of fruit and vegetables. People with diabetes should be able to enjoy food and eat a wide variety of foods as part of a healthy diet.

I advise people to take regular physical activity too.

Don't people need injections?

Yes, people with Type 1 diabetes have daily insulin injections, which are vital. Most patients I see give themselves two to four injections daily.

If you have Type 1 diabetes, you must learn to count your carbohydrate intake so that you can match the amount of insulin you take to the amount of carbohydrate you eat. This can take time to learn and get used to, and I encourage anyone who has concerns or questions to talk it over with me or one of my colleagues.

What's the treatment for Type 2 diabetes?

For most people with Type 2 diabetes, treatment involves lifestyle changes, such as a healthier diet, weight loss and increased physical activity. Some patients also need to take tablets and/or insulin to achieve normal blood glucose levels.

Can people with diabetes eat sugar and sweets?

Many people I see ask me about that! People with diabetes don't have to miss out completely on sweets and chocolate. It is all about balancing food, activity and insulin. People with diabetes should aim to have a diet low in sugar – particularly non-milk extrinsic sugars, as these cause blood sugar levels to rise quickly. It is also important to remember that very sugary foods are bad for teeth.

Why is it good for people with diabetes to exercise regularly?

Physical activity has many benefits, including improving diabetes control and helping to prevent some of the long-term complications of diabetes.

One of the reasons why more people are developing diabetes today is the increase in people who are overweight. So I advise everyone to be active and keep their weight under control.

DENTAL CARIES

Dental caries is also known as tooth decay and occurs when bacterial processes damage the hard structure of a tooth. The surface of the tooth breaks down progressively, resulting in a hole in the tooth called a dental cavity. If left untreated, the disease can lead to pain, tooth loss and infection. Dental caries is one of the most common diseases throughout the world.

Tooth decay is usually caused by a build-up of plaque, which is formed when food, saliva and bacteria combine on the surface of the teeth. Plaque gives a furry feeling on the teeth. When the plaque is exposed to sugar, acid is created and this damages tooth enamel and causes tooth decay.

Children and adolescents are particularly at risk of tooth decay and it is a common cause of tooth loss in younger people. The reason why young people are more at risk is that the enamel on their teeth, which have just emerged, is not very strong and so it is susceptible to acid attack. It is vital to establish good oral hygiene practices in childhood, as these habits will have a long-lasting impact on future dental health.

Risk factors for dental caries

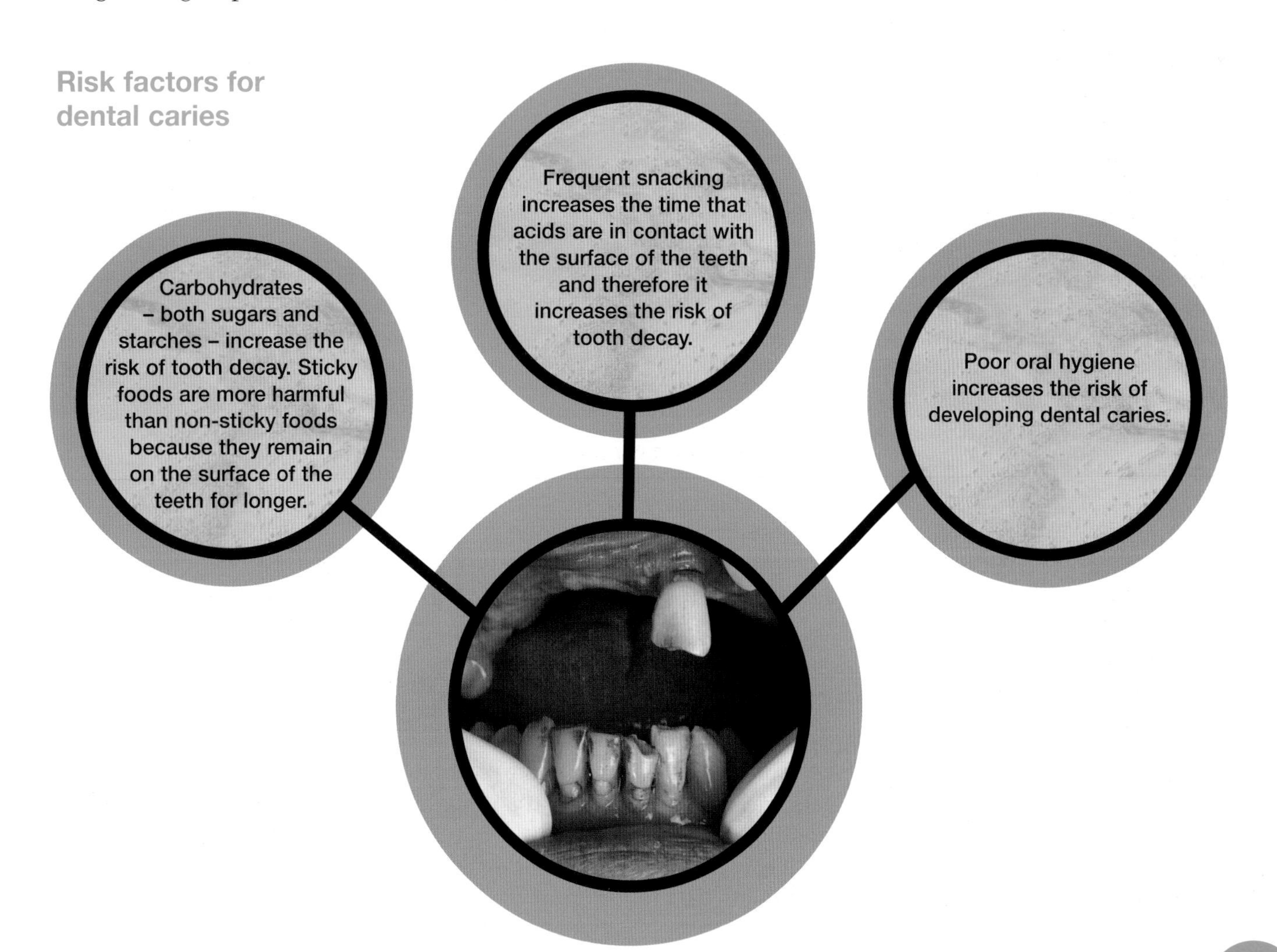

Diet and lifestyle advice to prevent dental caries

Good oral hygiene

Good oral hygiene includes making sure that plaque is removed from teeth effectively by correctly brushing teeth and using dental floss.

Diet

Eating nutritious meals and avoiding snacking between meals are important in protecting against dental caries. The supply of sugar in the mouth, and therefore the amount of acid in the mouth, is minimised.

Some foods, such as milk and dairy products, may protect against dental caries, since they appear to reduce acid in the mouth. Milk and cheese are both rich in calcium and eating these foods may encourage good tooth development.

Drinking water increases the flow of saliva, which neutralises the acid produced by plaque.

Dentist

Visiting the dentist regularly, preferably every six months, for routine check-ups, treatment if necessary, and advice, helps to maintain high standards of dental hygiene.

Fluoride

Fluoride also has a role to play in protecting teeth against decay. In some areas fluoride is present in drinking water, and studies have shown that there are fewer cases of dental caries in these areas.

If fluoride is taken when teeth are developing, as in the case of young children, it is incorporated into the structure of the tooth and gives added protection against acid damage. Parents of young children should seek advice from their dentist to find out if fluoride supplements should be given. It is possible to take too much fluoride, which can result in mottling of the tooth enamel. However, this only occurs in areas where there is an excessive amount of natural fluoride in the water.

Toothpaste and mouthwash with added fluoride help to protect the surface of teeth and should be used regularly as recommended.

ACTIVITY 7

Justify the following advice as a way to improve dental health.

- If eating sweets, eat them all at once rather than grazing on them throughout the day.
- Brush your teeth twice a day using fluoride toothpaste.
- Include dairy products as a regular part of your diet.

IRON DEFICIENCY ANAEMIA

Iron is required for the formation of haemoglobin, which is responsible for transporting oxygen around the body in red blood cells. A lack of iron in the blood can lead to iron deficiency anaemia. This results in less oxygen being transported to cells and tissues, giving rise to symptoms such as weakness, faintness, dizziness, lethargy and sometimes headaches, palpitations and sore gums. Someone who is anaemic may look pale.

Although anyone can become anaemic, anaemia most commonly affects growing children, adolescents (particularly girls), women and older people. Pregnant women must watch out for anaemia, as pregnancy is a time when the body may be lacking in iron. Vegetarians must plan their diet carefully to ensure that they get enough iron from food other than meat.

Risk factors for iron deficiency anaemia

A normal balanced diet should provide enough iron for the body's needs, but there are a variety of reasons why an individual may develop anaemia, as shown here and on page 50.

Dietary factors

Iron is found in liver, meat, beans, nuts, dried fruit (such as apricots), whole grains (such as brown rice), fortified breakfast cereals, soybean flour and most dark green leafy vegetables (e.g. watercress and curly kale). Not eating enough of these foods can be a cause of iron deficiency anaemia. An adequate intake of vitamin C is essential to ensure that iron from plant sources is aborbed by the body.

Most people in the UK get enough iron from their diet. However, if the amount of iron in someone's diet is only just adequate, other factors can result in anaemia. These factors include heavy menstruation in adolescent girls and women, pregnancy, or a growth spurt in children. Restricted or poorly planned diets may not contain enough iron.

Poor absorption of iron by the body

Some conditions of the intestine lead to poor absorption of various foods, including iron.

Some chemicals found naturally in food, such as phytates in certain fibre-rich foods and tannins in tea, can interfere with the way iron is absorbed.

Menstruation

Anaemia is common in women of all ages who have heavy periods, as the amount of iron they eat may not be enough to replace the iron lost. Iron deficiency anaemia is more likely to develop if a woman has heavy periods and eats a diet low in iron.

Pregnancy

Anaemia is common in pregnant women, as a developing fetus needs iron and will take it from the mother. Anaemia is more likely to develop during pregnancy if the diet is low in iron.

Periods of rapid growth – another risk factor for anaemia

During childhood and adolescence the body demands more iron and so there is a higher risk of iron deficiency anaemia. The diet may not be providing enough iron to meet increased need during these periods of rapid growth.

Introducing cows' milk into a baby's diet before it is twelve months old can lead to iron deficiency anaemia. This is because cows' milk is low in iron, which is needed for infant growth.

Children between the ages of one and three are at risk of iron deficiency anaemia, as most no longer consume iron-fortified formula milk and infant cereal, and do not eat enough iron-rich foods to make up the difference. Also, children in this age group tend to drink a lot of cows' milk, which is low in iron.

Boys are at risk of developing iron deficiency anaemia during the first stages of puberty, due to rapid growth, and girls are at higher risk due to menstrual blood loss and smaller iron stores. Also, many girls tend to consume a diet low in iron as they are more likely to adopt a vegetarian diet than boys of the same age.

ACTIVITY 8

a Write down three good sources of iron.

b Discuss why iron would be particularly important for:
- an adolescent girl
- a young child
- a pregnant woman.

c Give two reasons why vitamin C should be included in the diet with iron.

d Plan, make and evaluate a main meal rich in iron.

Diet and lifestyle advice on iron

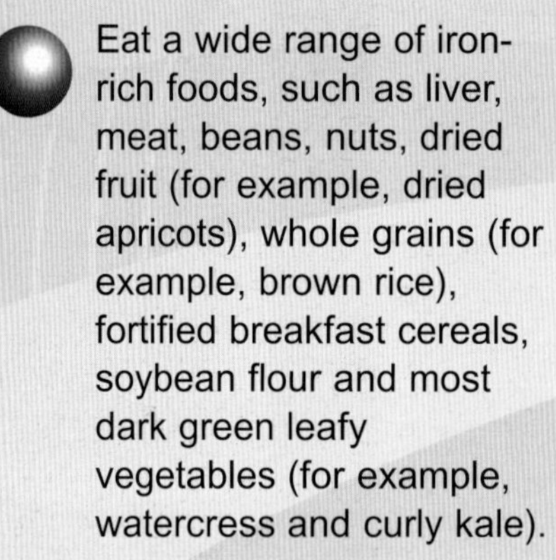

- Eat a wide range of iron-rich foods, such as liver, meat, beans, nuts, dried fruit (for example, dried apricots), whole grains (for example, brown rice), fortified breakfast cereals, soybean flour and most dark green leafy vegetables (for example, watercress and curly kale).
- Eat plenty of foods rich in vitamin C, such as peppers, broccoli, Brussel sprouts, sweet potatoes, oranges and kiwi fruit. Vitamin C helps the body to absorb iron from the foods eaten.
- Infants under twelve months should not be given cows' milk as a main drink. Breast milk or specially fortified infant formula milk are the only suitable main drinks. Iron-rich foods should be introduced during weaning after six months.
- Ensure that vegan or vegetarian diets include a good range of iron-rich foods, other than meat. Careful meal planning is essential, since iron from plant sources is less readily absorbed by the body than iron from meat sources.
- Do not take iron supplements unless advised to do so by a doctor. High doses of iron can be dangerous, especially in young children.

OBESITY

The World Health Organisation defines overweight and obesity as:

> "abnormal or excessive fat accumulation that may impair health."

Obesity happens when more calories are eaten than are burned off over a period of time and the extra energy from food is stored as fat. Fast foods, high-calorie snacks and large portions all make it easy to take in more energy than needed and obesity has become one of the most serious medical problems of the Western world.

RISK FACTORS FOR OBESITY	OBESE PEOPLE MAY EXPERIENCE THESE HEALTH PROBLEMS
• Family history of obesity • Genetic factors affecting appetite, ***metabolic rate*** and how the body stores fat • Overeating • Irregular meals • Lack of daily physical activity • Medicines that can cause weight gain	• Poor body image and low self-esteem, which can lead to anxiety and depression • Difficulties breathing • Difficulties walking or running • Pain in the knees and back • Skin conditions such as acne • Gallstones • High blood pressure • High cholesterol • Diseases related to hardening of the arteries, such as heart attack and stroke • Type 2 diabetes • Some types of cancer

What is metabolic rate?

The rate at which your body burns off calories from food and drink is known as your metabolic rate. Often, a person's metabolic rate increases during growth spurts and puberty, but by adulthood it is fairly steady. People who are very active generally have a higher metabolic rate than those who are inactive, because they burn off calories faster through energetic activity.

Body mass index

Calculating body mass index (BMI) is a way for medical practitioners to determine if someone is overweight or obese. BMI is calculated as weight (in kg) divided by height squared (m^2). For example, a person who weighs 65 kg and is 1.7 m tall has a BMI of 65 divided by (1.7 x 1.7), which works out as 22.5. This is in the normal range. A BMI of over 25 is classified as overweight and a BMI over 30 as obese.

This method of classifying body weight applies to adult men and women, except during pregnancy and older age. Children have their own BMI range, which takes age and gender as well as height and weight into account.

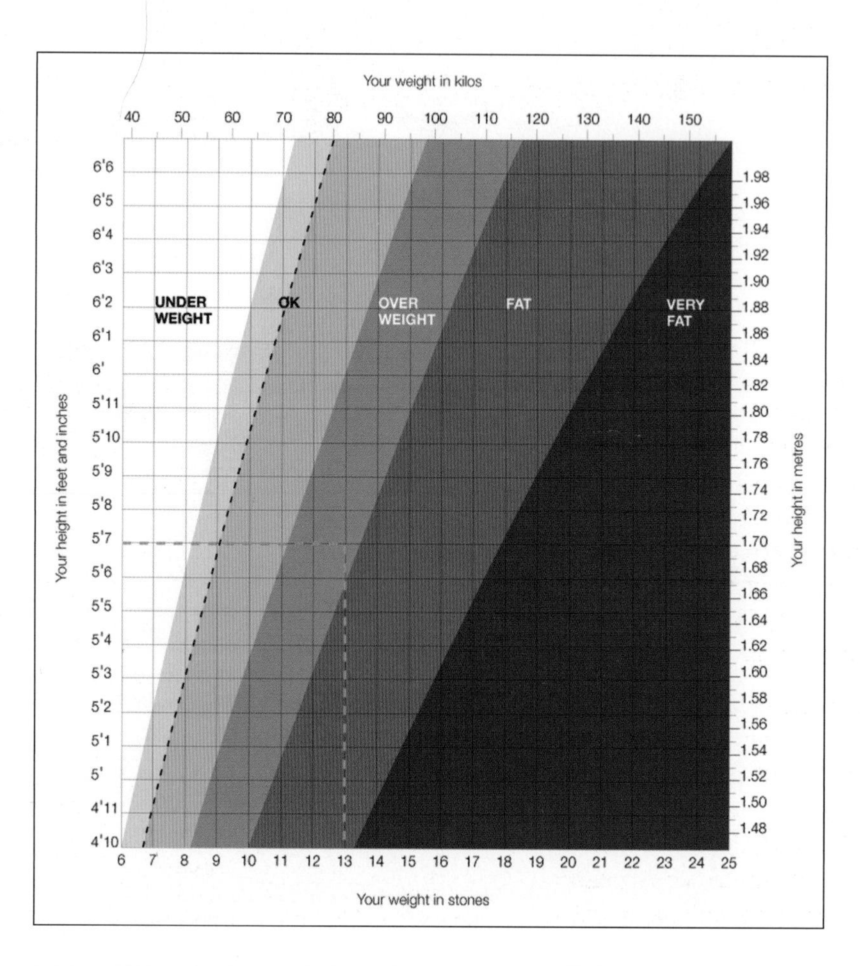

This chart from the Food Standards Agency allows people to check whether their weight is in the healthy range for their height. The chart is designed for adults.

PRESS RELEASE

An international conference, organised by the Health Promotion Agency (NI) and the Health Service Executive (RoI), was held in Belfast in November 2008. It was reported that the World Health Organisation's latest global projection is that by 2015 there will be approximately 2.3 billion adults overweight, with more than 700 million being obese. In Northern Ireland, 60 per cent of adults have a weight problem and as many as one in five are obese. Figures from 2006/07 show that approximately 22 per cent of Northern Ireland's primary school children are classed as overweight and obese.

In his opening remarks the Health Minister, Michael McGimpsey, said: 'There is no doubt that the obesity time bomb in Northern Ireland is ticking louder than ever. Our level of obesity, especially amongst our children, is incredibly worrying.'

The minister continued, 'Government cannot however tackle obesity on its own. I believe that we can certainly encourage and promote healthy eating and physical activity but as a society, we must take more individual responsibility for our own health outcomes.'

ACTIVITY 9

a In this press release, Michael McGimpsey says 'we must take more individual responsibility for our own health outcomes'. Explain how you could take more personal responsibility for your own health to reduce your risk of obesity.

b Investigate current Public Health Agency campaigns designed to reduce obesity in Northern Ireland. See www.publichealth.hscni.net for examples.

ACTIVITY 10

a Look back at the British Nutrition Foundation poster, The Role of Diet in Coronary Heart Disease, on page 42.

b Create your own poster on The Role of Diet in Obesity.

Diet and lifestyle advice to prevent obesity

To achieve and maintain a healthy weight, a balanced diet and physical activity are essential. By eating less than your body needs and exercising more, you force your body to use its existing fat stores for energy, and as the body burns its excess fat stores, you will lose weight.

Anyone who is obese would benefit greatly from seeking advice on how to lose weight, from a GP or dietitian. Table 5.1 highlights diet and lifestyle factors to consider in order to reduce obesity.

Table 5.1: Diet and lifestyle factors to reduce obesity

Diet	Lifestyle
Plan a diet that can be followed all the time and not just when trying to lose weight. • Trim the fat off meat. • Choose low-fat varieties of dairy and other products. • Increase intake of starchy foods instead of fatty ones. • Eat less of sugary foods. • Increase intake of fruit and vegetables and aim to eat five portions a day.	Physical activity has benefits not only for controlling body weight over the long term but also in controlling appetite. It has beneficial effects on the heart and blood which help to prevent cardiovascular disease.

OSTEOPOROSIS

Osteoporosis is a disease characterised by low bone mass and deterioration of the bone tissue, which leads to fragile bones and an increased risk of fracture. It is estimated that approximately one in two women and one in five men over 50 will fracture a bone because of osteoporosis (source: BUPA).

The condition occurs because, due to the natural process of ageing, from around the age of 35, more bone cells are lost than replaced. This results in a decrease in bone density. Broken wrists, hips and spinal bones are the most common fractures in people with osteoporosis. However, fractures can occur in any bone. Osteoporosis affects all age groups, but it is most common in ***post-menopausal*** women.

The growth, development and maintenance of healthy, strong bones depend on a good supply of several nutrients, including calcium, vitamin D, phosphorus and protein. The more of these nutrients deposited in bone during childhood and adolescence, the stronger the bone will be. If calcium intake is insufficient when bones are growing and developing, peak bone mass may be affected and the risk of bone fracture and osteoporosis in later life is increased.

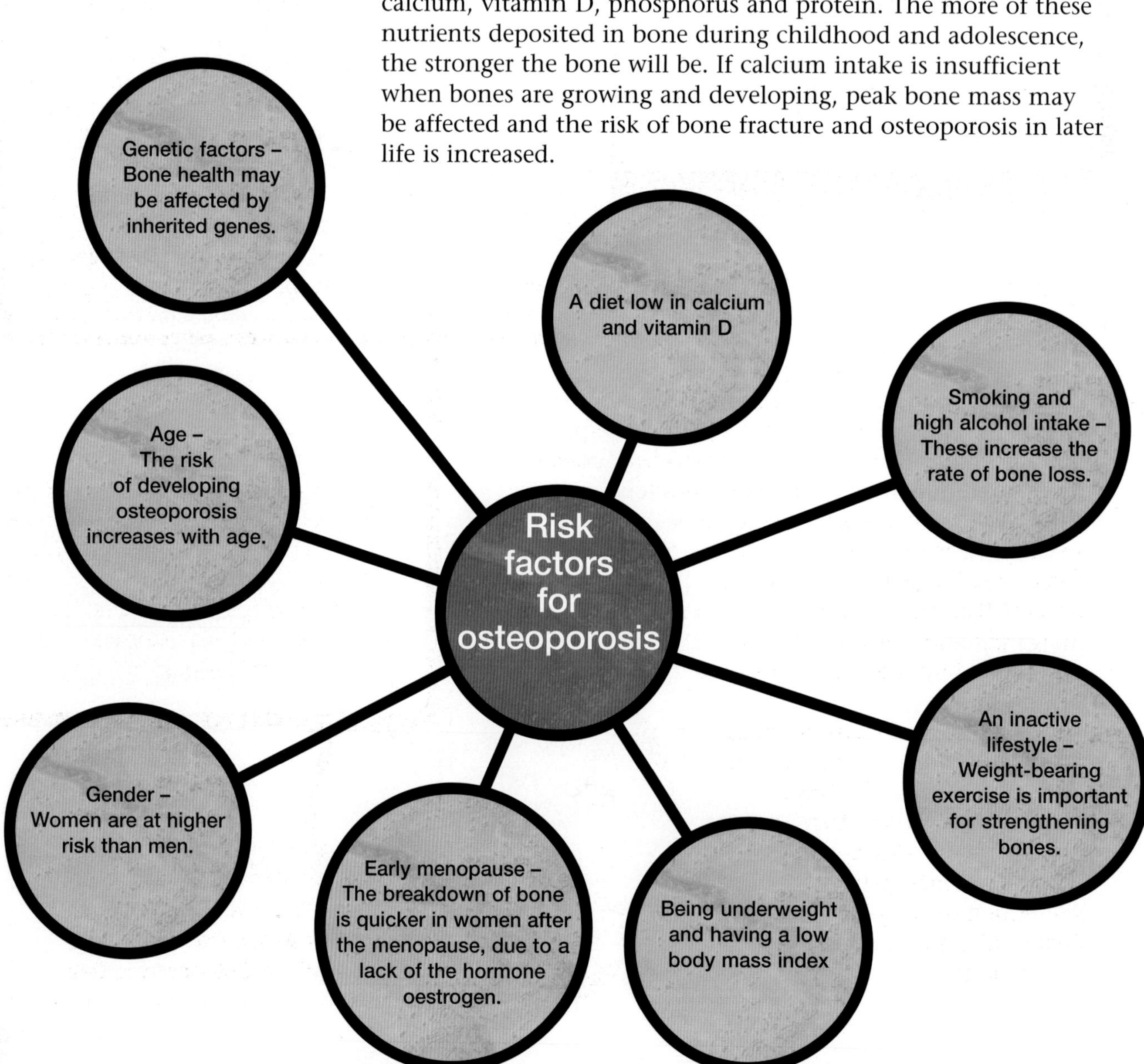

What is peak bone mass?

Peak bone mass is reached at the age of about 30–35 years and is the stage at which the bone is strongest. After this age, bone mass decreases, as more bone cells are lost than made. Having a good peak bone mass means that bones are stronger before natural loss begins and this reduces the risk of developing osteoporosis in later life.

Healthy bone consists of a strong mesh, like a solid sponge, made of protein and minerals, in particular calcium. This mesh is living tissue, which is constantly renewed by two types of cells. One type builds up new bone and the other breaks down old bone. As bone tissue is lost, the filaments of bone become thinner and can eventually disappear, leaving large spaces, and this causes bone to become weak, brittle and easily broken.

Bone section through hip

Solid bone

Weakened bone

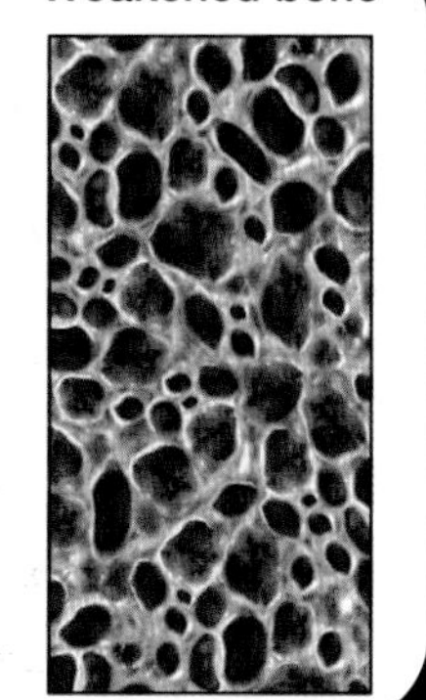

Diet and lifestyle advice to reduce the risk of osteoporosis

- Eat a healthy diet including foods rich in calcium and vitamin D. Vitamin D increases the absorption of calcium from foods, which helps to provide more calcium for building bones. Foods rich in calcium include milk and dairy products, such as hard cheese and yogurt, dried apricots or figs and some green leafy vegetables, such as watercress and curly kale. Foods rich in vitamin D include cod liver oil, oily fish such as sardines and herrings, margarine and egg yolks. Vitamin D is also formed by the action of sunlight on skin.
- Weight-bearing exercise, such as jogging, aerobics, tennis, weight-training, dancing and brisk walking, is good for strengthening bones. Exercise during childhood and adolescence helps to strengthen developing bones.
- Reduce alcohol intake.
- No smoking.

Did you know?

The teenage years are a very important time for bone growth and development. Approximately 30 per cent of all mineral deposited in the bones throughout life is deposited during adolescence. 90 per cent of the adult skeleton is formed by the age of eighteen and even earlier in girls.

ACTIVITY 11

Plan, make and evaluate a dish suitable to promote World Osteoporosis Day.

Chapter 6

Special diets

In this chapter you will learn about the following special diets:

- energy balance and weight management
- sports nutrition
- food allergy and food intolerance
- vegetarian and vegan.

After studying the chapter, you should be able to:

- suggest and justify diet and lifestyle advice for individuals with special diets
- plan, make and evaluate meals and menus and modify recipes to meet the dietary needs of individuals on special diets.

ENERGY

To perform these tasks, your body must have energy, the fuel it requires to stay alive. Energy is needed for a range of functions, including:

- making our muscles move and physical activity
- maintaining constant body temperature (37°C)
- bodily functions such as heartbeat, breathing and digestion
- growth and repair of body tissues
- meeting specific needs at particular times, for example, in pregnancy, during lactation and while we recover from illness.

Energy requirements

Energy requirements change and are affected by several factors:

- **Basal metabolic rate (BMR)**
  This is the amount of energy our body needs in order to maintain functions such as breathing and heartbeat and to keep at a constant temperature when it is totally at rest (for example, when we sleep). This accounts for 75 per cent of a person's energy needs. Young children have a proportionately high BMR for their size, to meet the demands of growth and development. Men usually have a higher BMR than women, as they tend to have greater muscle mass. Older adults usually have a lower BMR, as muscle mass tends to decrease with advancing age.

- **Level of physical activity**
  The body requires energy for all activities, including sitting, walking and exercising. People who exercise regularly or who have more physically demanding jobs need more energy. Those with sedentary occupations (for example, a call centre employee or an office worker) have lower energy requirements than people in very active occupations (for example, a farmer or a gym instructor).
- **Age**
  As individuals move through the lifespan, their energy requirements can vary. During childhood and adolescence energy requirements increase to meet the demands of growth and development. Ageing reduces energy needs, as growth has ceased and levels of physical activity may decline.
- **Gender**
  Males often have a larger body size and a higher BMR and require more energy to move.
- **Specific need**
  Female energy requirements increase moderately to meet the demands of pregnancy and lactation. A woman needs about 200 kilocalories more per day during the last trimester of pregnancy.
- **Thermogenic effect of food**
  This refers to an increase in energy expenditure after eating, while the body is digesting food.

The energy value of nutrients

The nutrients that provide the body with energy are carbohydrate, fat and protein.

The amount of energy in food is measured in kilocalories (kcal):

- 1 gram of fat provides 9 kilocalories
- 1 gram of carbohydrate provides 3.75 kilocalories
- 1 gram of protein provides 4 kilocalories
- 1 gram of alcohol provides 7 kilocalories (While alcohol is not a nutrient, it is broken down by the body to supply energy.)

100 g of pepperoni pizza provides approximately 195 kilocalories.

All foods and drinks containing calories provide energy. They have different energy values, depending on their carbohydrate, fat, protein or alcohol content. Foods with a high energy value often contain a large proportion of fat or sugar – but it is important to consider the nutritional implications of eating a diet high in fat and sugar. The best advice is to meet the majority of our energy needs from complex carbohydrates. They are a good source of slow release energy, which helps to keep blood sugar levels constant and leads to a feeling of fullness. They also provide other nutrients, such as B group vitamins, which assist in energy release from cells.

ACTIVITY 1

Use the information in tables 6.1 and 6.2 to complete a graph displaying the EARs of energy throughout the lifespan. Use your graph to answer these questions:

- Who has the highest energy requirements in the lifespan? Why?
- Who has the lowest energy requirements in the lifespan? Why?
- How do male and female energy requirements vary? Explain.
- How do energy requirements vary throughout the lifespan? Explain.

Estimated average requirements (EARs)

An EAR is an estimate of the average amount of energy, or of a nutrient, required by people in a particular age group. Approximately 50 per cent of people in the group require less, and 50 per cent require more, than the average amount. Tables 6.1 and 6.2 show the EARs of energy (kilocalories) for children and adolescents up to 18 years old, and the EARS for men and women with low activity levels.

Table 6.1: EARs of energy for children and adolescents

Age	Boys (kcal per day)	Girls (kcal per day)
0–3 months	545	515
4–6 months	690	645
7–9 months	825	765
10–12 months	920	865
1–3 years	1,230	1,165
4–6 years	1,715	1,545
7–10 years	1,970	1,740
11–14 years	2,220	1,845
15–18 years	2,755	2,110

Table 6.2: EARs of energy for adults

Age	Men (kcal per day)	Women (kcal per day)
19–49 years	2,550	1,940
50–59 years	2,550	1,900

To maintain a constant weight we need to balance energy taken in as food with the energy we expend.

Energy balance and weight management

The key to maintaining a healthy body weight is to balance energy intake from food with energy expenditure. It is crucial to remember that, while being overweight can increase a person's risk of developing

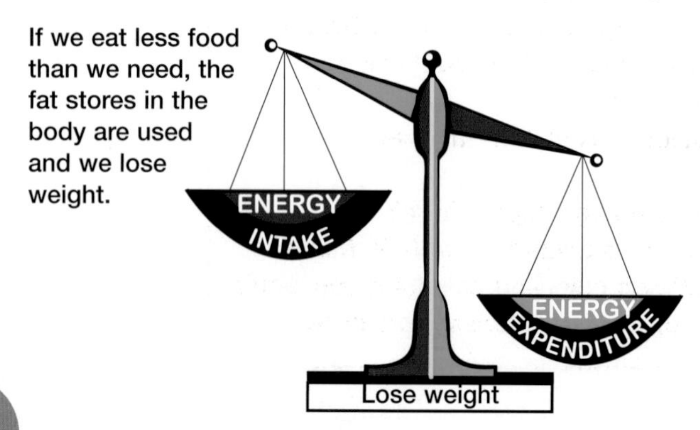

If we eat less food than we need, the fat stores in the body are used and we lose weight.

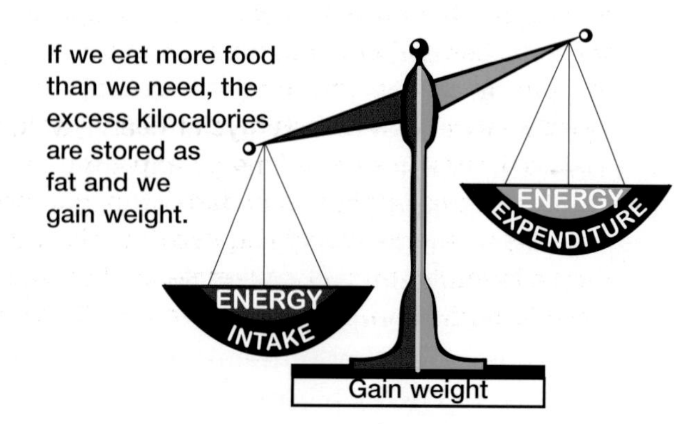

If we eat more food than we need, the excess kilocalories are stored as fat and we gain weight.

other dietary disorders, such as diabetes and coronary heat disease, being underweight can also have a negative impact on health.

In terms of weight management, it is important to consume foods that are nutrient-dense rather than energy-dense, in order to ensure that we meet our energy needs without taking in unnecessary kilocalories and so putting on weight. Examples of nutrient-dense foods are: wholegrain breads and cereals, low-fat dairy products, fruit and vegetables, lean meat, pasta, rice and pulses.

The energy intake needed to achieve weight loss depends on a range of factors, including the amount of weight to be lost and the amount of physical activity undertaken. Anyone trying to lose weight should seek advice from a GP, surgery nurse or dietitian. Most adult weight reduction diets provide between 1000 and 1500 kilocalories per day, and healthy weight loss should not exceed 1 kg per week. Children and adolescents who are still growing should aim to maintain energy balance rather than lose weight.

Being overweight can have a negative impact on health and over time may develop into obesity, a major dietary disorder in the UK.

ACTIVITY 2

a Explain how following the advice from the 'eatwell plate' (page 6) could help people to manage their weight.

b Discuss the '8 tips for eating well' (page 8) as a way of helping people to manage their weight.

Meal Planning for weight management

1 Follow the Food Standards Agency's '8 tips for eating well' and guidelines on the 'eatwell plate'.

2 Eat a healthy, balanced breakfast, as this prevents snacking and grazing through the day.

3 Plan meals and snacks in advance to ensure that healthy food is available when you need it.

4 Give consideration to portion sizes.

5 Aim to meet the '5 a day target' for fruit and vegetables. Include them at every meal, as they are nutritious but low in calories.

6 Choose foods that are low in fat and sugar, and limit salty and sugary snacks. Read the nutrition panel on food labels to determine if the food is a healthy option.

ACTIVITY 3

a Complete a 'Physical Activity Diary' over the period of a week.

b Evaluate your level of activity against advice from the Public Health Agency (formerly the Health Promotion Agency for Northern Ireland): see www.getalifegetactive.com

c Investigate the number of kilocalories used in performing various activities. Group the activities as high, moderate or low in energy expenditure. You could ask your PE teacher to help you or refer to one of these websites:
- www.eatwell.gov.uk/healthydiet/healthyweight/caloriecalculator/?lang=en
- www.fitness2live.co.uk/energy-expenditure

d What activities might you undertake to increase your energy expenditure?

e How much energy would you use if participating in this activity for 10/30/60 minutes?

f Pick a favourite treat (for example, a chocolate bar) and calculate how long you would need to participate in your chosen activity to burn up the kilocalories it provides.

ACTIVITY 4

Plan, make and evaluate a daily menu suitable for an athlete.

ACTIVITY 5

Compile a nutrition/health profile of a sportsperson of your choice. Work in small groups to identify the focus of your research and present any interesting findings to your class.

SPORTS NUTRITION

Healthy eating and regular physical activity are important for everyone, but for people involved in sport, the quality of their diet and how much they eat and drink can have a dramatic impact on their performance. Estimated energy requirements increase substantially for athletes, to meet the body's extra demands during exercise. The amount of energy needed depends on the intensity, duration, frequency and type of exercise and on the age, gender, level of fitness and body fat stores of the individual.

Carbohydrate

A diet based on complex carbohydrates, such as bread, pasta, rice and beans, is important because these are nutrient-dense, filling and low in fat. Carbohydrate is stored in the muscles and liver as ***glycogen***.

For endurance and stamina it is essential to maintain glycogen stores because, once these stores are used up, muscles cannot work efficiently and performance is affected. The best way to keep up glycogen levels is to eat a low-fat, high-carbohydrate light meal, two to three hours before exercise; this allows time for digestion and excretion to occur. After exercising, it is important to replenish glycogen stores with low-fat, high-carbohydrate snacks.

On average, a sportsperson uses 500–1000 kcal per day more than a sedentary adult. Therefore a small amount of sugary foods and drinks can be consumed. These are not bulky or filling; they provide short bursts of energy quickly and can be an effective way for athletes to top up carbohydrate intake.

While most sportspeople maintain a high-carbohydrate diet, those involved in endurance events may increase carbohydrate intake by more than 70 per cent in the three days preceding an event. This is known as 'carbohydrate loading' and, combined with a specialist training programme, it can increase glycogen stores and maximise performance.

Meal Planning for sport

1 **Plan meals rich in complex carbohydrates: pasta, bread, rice, beans, pulses and potatoes.**

2 **Keep up the protein content of the diet with meat, fish, shellfish, dairy products, eggs, pulses and nuts.**

3 **Plan meals and snacks that include a range of fruit and vegetables – fresh, frozen, canned, or dried.**

4 **Use sugary and fatty foods in small quantities.**

5 **Take care with timing and portioning of meals.**

6 **Plan regular healthy snacks to meet increased demands for nutrients.**

Protein

Most sportspeople can meet their protein requirements by following a balanced diet. Main meals should provide some protein, for example, meat, fish, poultry, eggs, dairy products, beans, pulses, quorn, tofu and nuts. Only athletes involved in heavy training may need to increase their protein intake in order to gain muscle. This would apply, for example, to weightlifters or those taking part in endurance events, such as marathon runners,

It is important for all sportspeople to consume enough carbohydrate as fuel; otherwise, their body will use protein as a source of energy and its role in maintaining and repairing tissues, including muscle, will be compromised.

Fat

A high-fat diet makes it difficult to meet carbohydrate requirements and could affect weight management and energy balance. In particular, saturated fat intake should be monitored.

Vitamins and minerals

A balanced diet with a variety of foods from the five food groups should provide the vitamins required for good health. The B group vitamins are particularly relevant for people participating in sport, since they assist with the release of energy from food. A diet that includes fortified cereals, meat, dairy products, eggs, pulses and green leafy vegetables should provide enough of these vitamins.

Sportspeople need good iron stores to ensure that oxygen can be transported around the body in their blood and to boost energy stores. They are advised to eat readily available sources of iron, such as lean red meat. Sportspeople following a vegetarian diet should eat pulses and green leafy vegetables, in combination with taking vitamin C.

Calcium intake should be maintained as, regardless of the sport, everyone should be aiming to achieve and maintain a good peak bone mass. This contributes to a stronger skeleton, makes bones less susceptible to damage and helps to repair body tissue.

Fluid balance

Before, during and after an event, athletes must take in fluid to replace what they have lost by sweating. Water is essential to restore fluid balance in the body, particularly the blood. People participating in sport need to drink more than the six to eight glasses advised for the general population.

Sports drinks have been developed which claim to offer additional benefits, as they can contain sugar and sodium and are easy to drink, often increasing the rate of ***rehydration***. They are suitable for people involved in vigorous physical activity, but should not be consumed by others, as regular consumption could lead to weight gain and dental caries.

ACTIVITY 6

a Take on the role of a sports coach trying to improve the performance of athletes by evaluating a range of sports and energy drinks. You could make a table, as shown below, to organise your work.

b Do sports/energy drinks perform a specific function? Should they be consumed as a regular drink? Explain your answers.

Name of drink	Ingredients	Advice on label	Claim on label	Evidence for/against the claim	Your opinion/ verdict

ACTIVITY 7

As a class, come up with a range of questions to ask a person with a food allergy or food intolerance. Invite such a person to the class and interview them about how their allergy or food intolerance impacts on their diet and lifestyle.

FOOD ALLERGY AND FOOD INTOLERANCE

According to the British Dietetic Association, as many as one in five people believe themselves to be allergic or intolerant to a food. In reality, less than one per cent of the adult population actually has a food allergy.

Some people diagnose themselves with a food allergy or ***food intolerance*** and exclude certain foods from their diet. By doing so, they run the risk of developing nutrient deficiencies. To avoid this problem, anyone with a concern should seek medical advice rather than trying to treat themselves. Food allergy and food intolerance are both classified as types of food sensitivity.

Food allergy

An allergy to a specific food causes the body's immune system to react. Someone with a severe food allergy can experience a life-threatening reaction. Individuals with food allergies need to be extremely careful about what they eat.

Any food can cause a food allergy reaction. However, most allergic reactions are caused by one of the following:

- cereals containing ***gluten*** (including wheat, rye, barley and oats)
- eggs
- fish and shellfish
- milk
- nuts (including brazil nuts, hazelnuts, almonds and walnuts)
- peanuts
- sesame seeds
- soya
- sulphur dioxide or sulphites, used as additives in food.

Nuts can cause severe allergic reactions, even if there is only a trace of nuts, for example, in a sauce or biscuit.

Labelling legislation states that, if any of these ingredients are added to pre-packed foods, they must be indicated clearly on the label.

The most common symptoms of an allergic reaction include:

- coughing
- dry, itchy throat and tongue
- itchy skin or rash
- nausea and feeling bloated
- diarrhoea and/or vomiting
- wheezing and shortness of breath
- swelling of the lips and throat
- runny or blocked nose
- sore, red and itchy eyes.

Symptoms can appear within minutes, or up to several hours after someone has eaten the food they are allergic to.

Anaphylaxis

People with severe allergies can have a reaction called anaphylaxis (pronounced anna-fill-axis), sometimes called ***anaphylactic shock***. When someone has an anaphylactic reaction, they can have symptoms in different parts of the body at the same time, including rashes, swelling of the lips and throat, difficulty breathing and a rapid fall in blood pressure and loss of consciousness.

Anaphylaxis can be fatal if it isn't treated immediately, usually with an injection of adrenaline (epinephrine). This is why it's extremely important for someone with a severe allergy to take their medication with them wherever they go.

ACTIVITY 8

a Use the Food Standards Agency website (www.food.gov.uk) to research different types of food intolerance and allergy.

b Select one food intolerance or allergy and complete a factfile of advice about it for the school nurse, canteen or Home Economics department.

Food intolerance

Food intolerance doesn't involve the immune system and is generally not life-threatening. But if someone eats a food they are intolerant to, this could make them feel ill or affect their long-term health. Two examples of food intolerances are ***lactose*** intolerance (below) and gluten intolerance (see page 64).

Lactose intolerance

Lactose is a sugar found naturally in milk. In the body, it is broken down by an enzyme called lactase, so that it can be absorbed into the bloodstream. Lactose intolerance is caused by a shortage of lactase. When someone doesn't have enough of this enzyme, lactose isn't absorbed properly from the gut. The main symptoms are stomach cramps, bloating, flatulence and diarrhoea.

In the UK and Ireland, about five in 100 of the adult population are lactose intolerant. Doctors advise them to avoid consuming cows' milk. However, some products made from cows' milk can be eaten, including hard cheeses such as cheddar, which contain little lactose, and yogurt, since the live bacteria it contains promotes the digestion of lactose. Some people with lactose intolerance use soya milk as an alternative to cows' milk.

Any changes to the diet, regarding the exclusion of a food group, should only be made following advice from a doctor.

Soya beans and some of the products made from them. Soya milk is high in protein and fortified with vitamins and minerals.

Gluten intolerance (coeliac disease)

Coeliac disease is an 'auto-immune disease', where the body produces antibodies that attack its own tissues. An attack is caused by a protein called gluten, found in cereals such as wheat, rye and barley. Symptoms of coeliac disease include nausea, flatulence, tiredness, constipation, reduced growth and skin problems.

Mismanagement of coeliac disease can result in long-term effects such as malnutrition, anaemia and bone disease. It can also cause growth problems in children.

Gluten is used in a wide variety of foods, including bread, pasta, pizza, pastry and cakes. It is essential that individuals with coeliac disease carefully check the list of ingredients on food labels. For example, there may be gluten in sausages, burgers, sauces, batter and breadcrumbs.

Foods to include for people with coeliac disease

- Rice
- Potatoes
- Corn
- Meat, fish and poultry
- Pulses
- Fruit and vegetables
- Nuts
- Gluten-free pasta, bread and other products

Foods to avoid for people with coeliac disease

- Wheat (breads, cakes, biscuits, pasta, breadcrumbs, batter)
- Barley (soup)
- Oats (breakfast cereals, cereal bars)
- Rye (bread)
- Processed meat (sausages, meat pies)
- Baking powder
- Stock cubes

NB Products labelled 'wheat-free' may contain other cereals, such as rye or barley. Make sure that they are also labelled 'gluten-free'.

Meal Planning for food allergy and food intolerance

1 Exclude the food causing the problem from all meals.

2 Check the labels on all food products, including on regular purchases, since the ingredients may have changed.

3 Identify replacements for foods that cannot be eaten, to ensure a balance of nutrients in the diet.

4 Modify recipes and plan meals to meet the specific dietary requirements. Organisations such as Coeliac UK (www.coeliac.co.uk) offer an extensive range of resources, including shopping directories and recipe ideas.

5 Sustain an interest in food by planning creative and interesting meals.

ACTIVITY 9

Explain a range of factors that should be considered by individuals with the following food intolerances, to ensure a balanced diet:

- lactose intolerance
- coeliac disease.

VEGETARIAN AND VEGAN

People choose a vegetarian diet for a variety of reasons, including concern about the environment or animal welfare and because they believe it is healthier. For some people, being vegetarian is part of their religion. Vegetarian diets can be defined in many ways and can mean different things to different people. Some people include fish or chicken; others avoid meat but still eat dairy products and eggs.

The most commonly adopted vegetarian diets are:

- lacto-ovo vegetarian – eats dairy products and eggs, but does not eat meat
- vegan – does not eat dairy products, eggs, meat or any animal by-products such as honey or gelatine.

Whichever type of vegetarian diet people follow, they must make sure that they achieve optimal health by consuming foods that provide all the nutrients the body needs. A well-planned and varied vegetarian diet provides sufficient energy and nutrients, as long as the foods that are excluded are replaced with suitable alternatives. Table 6.3 on page 66 shows the nutrients that need to be considered when following a vegetarian or vegan diet.

It is important that vegetarian dishes provide a range of colours, textures and flavours, as shown in this fragrant pumpkin coconut curry.

ACTIVITY 10

Use the information in table 6.3 (page 66) and from Chapters 2 and 5 to help you answer the questions below. You could also use websites such as:

- www.vegsoc.org
- www.food.gov.uk
- www.vegansociety.com
- www.nutrition.org

a Why is vitamin B_{12} often deficient in a vegetarian diet and how can this be prevented?
b How can iron needs be met in a vegetarian diet?
c Why should vegetarians be encouraged to increase their vitamin C intake?
d Why is a balanced vegetarian diet often low in fat and what benefits to health does this offer?
e Why is a balanced vegetarian diet higher in NSP and what benefits does this offer?
f How can a vegetarian diet offer protection against diseases such as coronary heart disease and obesity?

ACTIVITY 11

Plan, make and evaluate a range of nutritious meals for vegans and vegetarians.

Table 6.3: The nutrients to consider when following a vegetarian or vegan diet.

Nutrient	Vegetarian diet	Vegan diet
Fat	• Vegetarians who consume a lot of dairy products, e.g. cheese, need to be careful not to consume too much saturated fat.	• Need to include a range of foods rich in unsaturated fats, which provide important essential fatty acids.
Protein	• Protein needs can be met if dairy products and eggs are consumed.	• Protein from plant sources is of low biological value. Plant foods need to be eaten in combination (e.g. beans on toast) to ensure that all the indispensable amino acids are provided. • Soya and quinoa are the only two plant sources of high biological value protein.
Calcium	• Vegetarians consuming milk and dairy products are likely to meet calcium requirements.	• Calcium from plant sources can be difficult for the body to absorb, due to the presence of phytates or oxalates. Vegans should eat foods fortified with calcium, e.g. white bread, soya milk/yogurts and breakfast cereals.
Iron	• Iron from non-haem sources, e.g. egg yolk, cereals, green leafy vegetables, nuts and pulses, is absorbed less efficiently than iron from meat. To promote absorption, these foods should be eaten with foods rich in vitamin C. • Tannins in tea can affect the absorption of iron and so tea should not be drunk with meals.	• Iron from non-haem sources, e.g. cereals, green leafy vegetables, nuts and pulses, is absorbed less efficiently than iron from meat. To promote absorption, these foods should be eaten with foods rich in vitamin C. • Tannins in tea can affect the absorption of iron and so tea should not be drunk with meals.
Vitamin D	• Vitamin D intake can be maintained by consuming eggs, whole milk and dairy products.	• Vegans can meet vitamin D requirements by eating cereals and reduced-fat spreads fortified with vitamin D. • It is essential to get exposure to sunlight to promote vitamin D synthesis in the skin.
Vitamin B_{12}	• Vitamin B_{12} can be obtained from milk, dairy products and eggs.	• Vegans must ensure that they include vitamin B_{12} in their diet, as it is not found in foods from plant sources. Fortified foods such as soya milk, meat alternatives and breakfast cereals are the best sources of vitamin B_{12} for those excluding all animal products. Vegans may be advised to use a vitamin B_{12} supplement.

Tofu is one alternative to meat.

Adopting a vegetarian diet – dos and don'ts

Don't ...

- give up meat and not replace it with other sources of important nutrients.
- depend only on dairy products as a replacement for meat.
- eat too many sugary or fatty foods.
- rely on ready-made vegetarian meals and convenience foods.
- exclude a food group from your diet.

Don't simply replace meat and vegetables with nothing and vegetables!

Do ...

- eat a variety of foods from the five food groups.
- eat fortified cereals for breakfast.
- exceed the '5 a day' target for fruit and vegetables.
- include alternatives to meat to ensure protein needs can be met, for example, soya, quinoa, tofu, beans, lentils, chickpeas, eggs, dairy products, nuts and seeds.
- enjoy a wide variety of food and try new foods, for example, soya, quinoa, quorn and pulses.

Two examples of tasty and interesting vegetarian meals are bean burrito, salad and dip and spaghetti bolognese made with quorn mince.

ACTIVITY 12

In small groups, research one source of protein suitable for vegetarians which could be eaten as an alternative to meat, such as textured vegetable protein (TVP), quorn, tofu. Produce a factsheet about it, considering these factors:

- nutritional value – especially as a source of protein
- cost
- availability
- versatility
- sensory appeal
- other benefits.

ACTIVITY 13

Using information obtained from classroom discussion, activities and research, respond to the following statements:

- statement a: A vegetarian diet closely matches the dietary recommendations for healthy eating.
- statement b: Eating a vegetarian diet is better for the environment.
- statement c: It is easy to become a junk food vegetarian.
- statement d: Eating meat may be a moral issue – but we all have the right to choose.

Chapter 7

The facts behind the issues

In this chapter you will learn about some issues related to Diet and Health. After studying the chapter, you should be able to discuss the potential impact of the following issues on health and lifestyle:

- fast and convenience foods
- nano foods
- superfoods
- functional and fortified foods.

ACTIVITY 1

a Evaluate your favourite fast food meal. You may want to consider the following criteria:
- nutritional value
- sensory appeal
- cost.

Can you think of any other criteria?

b Modify this fast food meal to make it more nutritious, and plan, make and evaluate your recipe.

FAST FOOD

Fast food is food that is prepared quickly and packaged so that it is portable enough either to eat on the premises or to take away to eat elsewhere. Types of fast food in the UK include burgers, fried chicken, pizza, fish and chips, and kebabs.

Fast food receives a lot of criticism, partly due to the fact that it tends to be energy-dense rather than nutrient-dense. However, effective marketing and the availability and affordability of fast food have all increased its popularity.

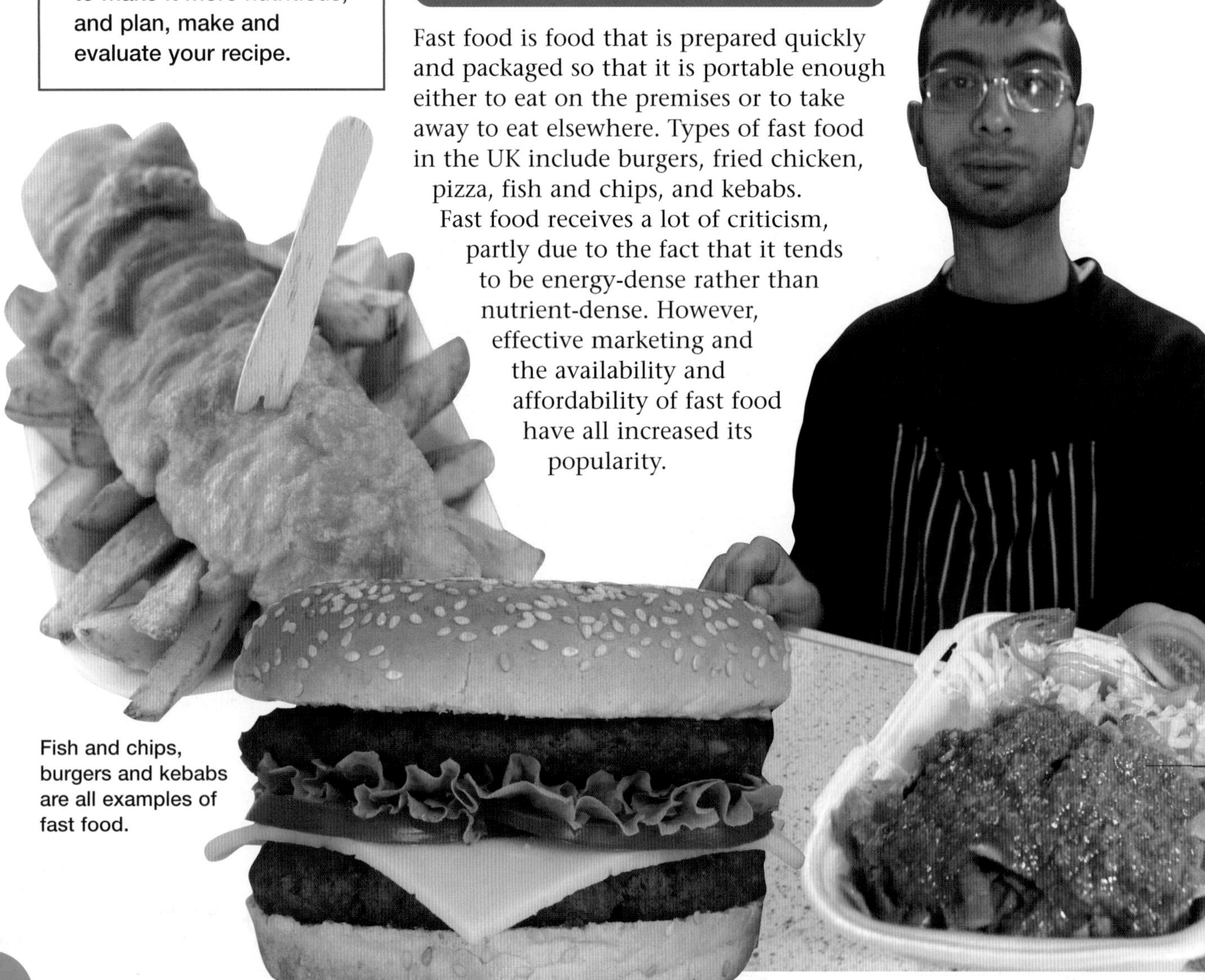

Fish and chips, burgers and kebabs are all examples of fast food.

ACTIVITY 2

a Identify a fast food meal that you eat regularly from a well-known fast food chain.

b Find information about the fast food meal, for example, from the company website or in-store leaflet. Also record the energy value of the meal (in kilocalories).

c Research the type and amount of physical activity you would need to take part in to expend the number of kilocalories you have consumed. You could ask your PE teacher to help you, or use these websites:

- www.eatwell.gov.uk/healthydiet/healthyweight/caloriecalculator/?lang=en
- www.fitness2live.co.uk/energy-expenditure

ACTIVITY 3

Identify and evaluate current promotional strategies being used by fast food producers to sell their food to target consumers.

ACTIVITY 4

Design a card called 'fast food facts' for teenagers to keep in their purse or wallet and which will help them to make healthy fast food choices.

How does a picture like this aim to make people want to buy pizza?

How does packaging increase the appeal of fast food?

ACTIVITY 5

Design a version of the 'eatwell plate' (page 6) which recommends examples of convenience foods that could be eaten for all the five food groups, to help consumers achieve a healthy and well-balanced diet.

Dried pasta is easy to store and can be cooked in a few minutes.

CONVENIENCE FOODS

Convenience foods are processed foods that are partially prepared already and require minimal preparation skills to use. Types of convenience foods include:

Cook-chill ready meals need only to be heated, as instructed on the packet.

- canned food, for example, tomatoes, beans, tuna
- cartons of food, for example, soup, sauces, fruit juice
- cook-chill food, for example, ready meals, processed meat, cheesecake
- dried food, for example, peas, herbs, pasta
- frozen food, for example, pastry, vegetables, ice cream
- jars of food, for example, simmer sauces, baby food, jam
- ready-to-eat food, for example, fruit salad, biscuits, sandwiches
- value-added side dishes, for example, mashed potato, garlic bread, stir-fry vegetables.

Ready-to-eat sandwiches save time, but not money.

Compared with in the past, many people work longer hours and have more choice about how to spend their free time. As a result, ease of use has become one of the main things that consumers look for when shopping for food and cooking. Convenience foods answer this need and are readily available. The change has led to more money being spent on food, but less time and fewer skills being given to preparing fresh ingredients.

Frozen peas are convenient and healthy.

In many cases, convenience foods make excellent use of technology. For example, frozen peas that have been picked and frozen in one day are as fresh and healthy to eat as if you had just picked them yourself. However, other convenience foods are highly processed. During the processing, nutrients like vitamins can easily be lost. Also, additives may be used to improve the food's sensory appeal.

ACTIVITY 6

a Suggest ways of using convenience foods to make a healthy meal for a range of situations, for example:
   - a children's birthday party
   - a main meal for a family on a budget
   - a weekend breakfast
   - a packed lunch.

b Plan, prepare and make one of these meals.

NANO FOODS

Nano foods came into being when developments in technology made it possible to manipulate the molecules in food in order to improve its sensory appeal, ***shelf life*** and health benefits. An example of nanotechnology, in relation to food, is the formulation of a product that has the taste and texture of mayonnaise without the calories.

At present, nanotechnology is in the developmental stages, but it is thought that it can be applied in all stages of food production, for example:

- in farming: to produce safer ***pesticides***
- in food processing: to limit the loss of nutrients during processing
- in packaging: to design packaging that prolongs the shelf life of food.

The main concerns associated with nanotechnology involve a lack of consumer confidence, together with questions about long-term risks to health and the environmental impact.

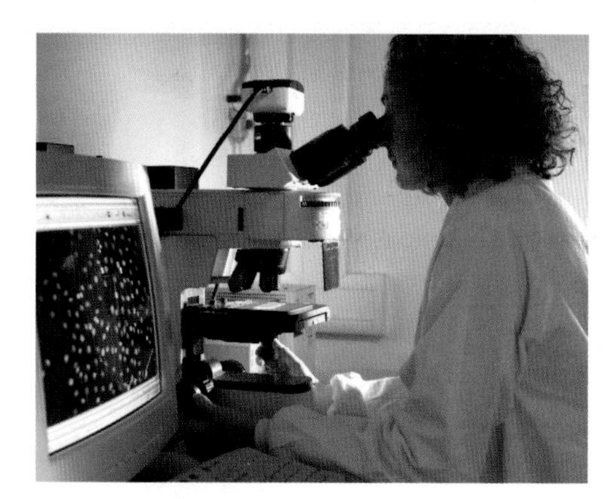

Nanotechnology deals with the tiniest dimensions, and so very powerful microscopes are needed.

ACTIVITY 7

Research a range of newspaper articles to establish current opinions about nano foods.

SUPERFOODS

Superfoods are difficult to categorise as there is currently no legal definition of the term. The foods are promoted by the media, supermarkets, food producers and food companies as providing large proportions of important nutrients and offering extra protection against disease. The main groups of foods advertised as superfoods include:

- fruit: for example, blueberries – a source of the antioxidant nutrient vitamin C
- vegetables: for example, broccoli – a source of the antioxidant nutrient vitamins A and C
- nuts: for example, brazil nuts – a source of the antioxidant nutrient selenium
- fish: for example, salmon – a source of the essential fatty acid Omega 3.

Some ***nutritionists*** are concerned that health claims made about superfoods may mislead consumers, particularly if these claims are not regulated by law or supported by scientific evidence. These nutritionists advise that we should eat a variety of foods from the five food groups, and not over-consume the 'special' foods in place of cheaper alternatives.

ACTIVITY 8

a Carry out research to identify a range of superfoods. For each:
- Establish the health claim being made.
- Determine the nutritional accuracy of the claim.
- Justify your assessment with evidence.
- Evaluate against other criteria, for example, cost, availability, ease of use, environmental impact.

b Select one superfood (for example, blueberry) and compare its nutritional value to a similar product not currently promoted as a superfood (for example, kiwi fruit).

c Design a superfood recipe resource to promote healthy eating. Be creative with its format. For example, you might compile a range of cookery cards to be distributed at a local supermarket or develop an online recipe book for your school website.

FUNCTIONAL FOODS

Functional foods are those developed to offer specific health benefits, beyond their usual nutritional value. The most commonly used include:

- margarines containing plant sterols, which are claimed to reduce cholesterol
- ***probiotics***, usually in the form of fermented milk or dairy products containing 'good bacteria', which are claimed to improve the health of the digestive system
- ***prebiotics***, usually carbohydrate products such as breakfast cereals rich in soluble NSP, which are said to promote the function of probiotics and help maintain a healthy digestive system.

Any claims made by the manufacturers of these foods must be reliable and scientifically sound. Also, advice must be offered to consumers about how to use the products in order to achieve the advertised benefit to health.

It should be remembered that many foods naturally promote good health. For example, oats are a valuable source of soluble fibre, which plays a positive role in reducing blood cholesterol levels. Functional foods, regardless of their value, should not be seen as a replacement for a balanced diet.

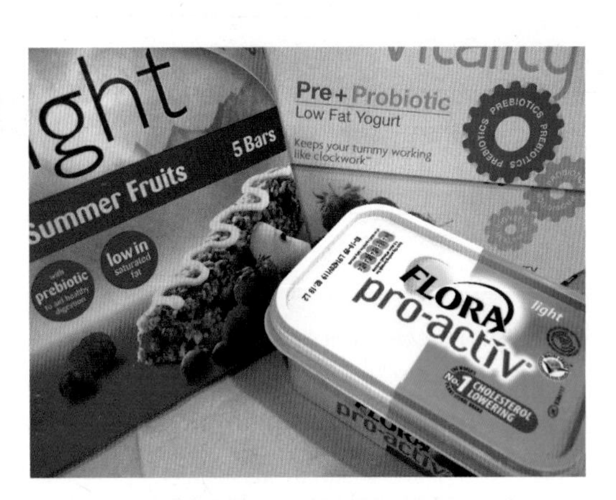

The health claims made on functional foods must be scientifically sound.

ACTIVITY 9

a Visit a supermarket to compile a list of functional foods. Focus on the range of products available, the price of products and the advertised benefits to health.

b Would you buy them?

FORTIFIED FOODS

Fortified foods are a type of functional food, as they are products that have been supplemented with nutrients, usually in the form of vitamins and minerals. The most common types of fortified products in the UK are staple foods such as bread, cereals and margarine.

Reasons why food is fortified include:

- **to enrich products for individuals with special diets**, for example:
  - soya products are fortified with vitamin B_{12} and calcium to meet the needs of vegans
  - infant formula milk is fortified with iron and vitamin D.
- **to enrich a staple food with a nutrient that it does not naturally contain**, for example:
  - vitamin A and vitamin D must, by law, be added to margarine, so that it matches butter in the nutrients it contains
  - calcium is added to soya dairy products, so that they match the nutrients in milk.
- **to replace nutrients lost during processing**, for example:
  - B group vitamins are added to brown and white flour, as bran is removed during processing.

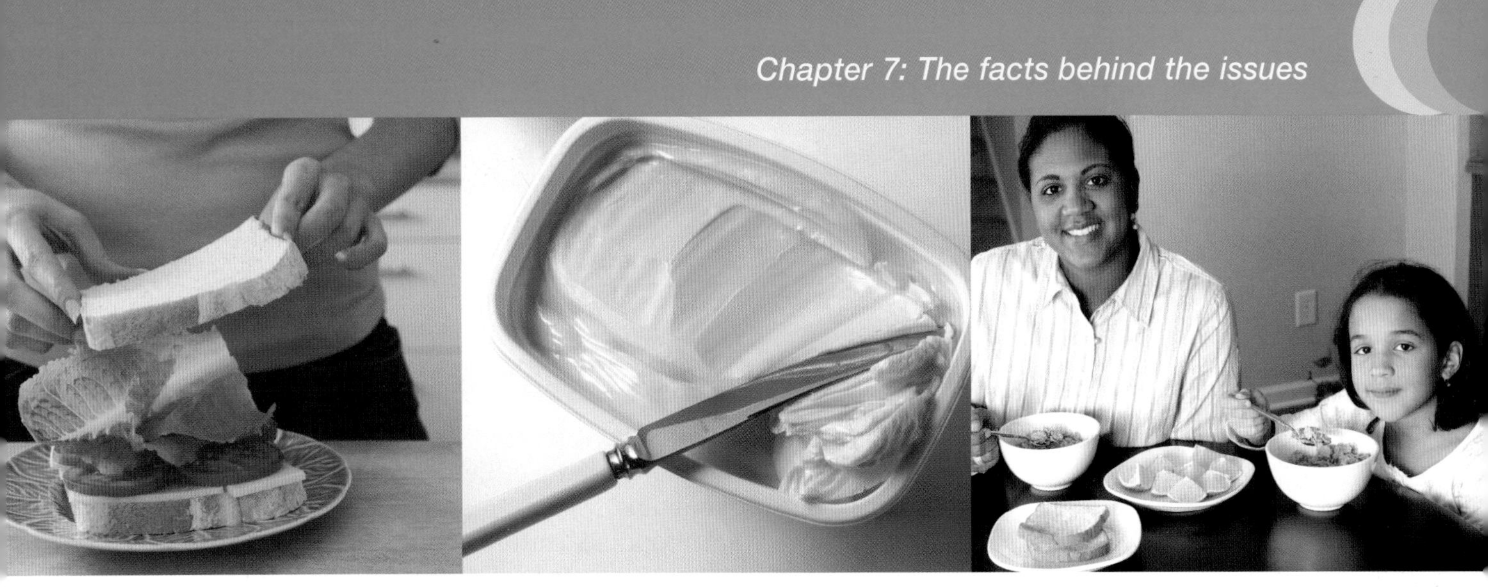

White bread, margarine and breakfast cereals are some examples of fortified foods.

- **to improve the nutritional status of a specific group of people, who may be deficient in a particular nutrient**, for example:
  - breakfast cereals are fortified to help young children in particular to meet their nutritional needs.
- **to prevent deficiency disorders**, for example:
  - anaemia
  - osteoporosis.

Across Europe, the fortification of foods is controlled by regulations on nutrition and health claims. There are rules about minimum levels of fortification and upper limits which must not be exceeded, for safety reasons. Supporters of fortified foods view them as a convenient way to encourage consumers to meet their nutritional requirements over time, as the products only need to be consumed little and often to be of value. People who oppose fortification view it as removing choice from consumers. They also warn that regularly overeating fortified food could result in excessive levels of intake.

ACTIVITY 10

Complete a survey to find out patterns of consumption of fortified foods in your class. Record the results, present them in graphs, and discuss your findings.

ACTIVITY 11

Carry out a class debate on one of the motions listed below, or on another motion given to you by your class teacher. Advice on how to carry out a debate is given on page 125.

- This house believes that not all fast food is junk food.
- This house supports the use of convenience foods as part of a healthy diet.
- This house believes that nano foods offer major benefits to health.
- This house disputes that superfoods exist.
- This house believes that functional foods are just a way for food companies to make money.
- This house would ban fortified foods.

Chapter 8

Keeping food safe

Section A: Diet and Health

In this chapter you will learn how to keep food safe. After studying the chapter, you should be able to:

- explain food safety in relation to:
  - personal hygiene
  - food purchase
  - food storage
  - food preparation
  - ages and stages
- discuss the symptoms, food sources and methods of control for the following food poisoning bacteria:
  - listeria
  - salmonella
  - staphylococcus aureus
- outline the protection offered to the consumer by:
  - the Food Safety (NI) Order 1991
  - the Environmental Health Officer.

PERSONAL HYGIENE

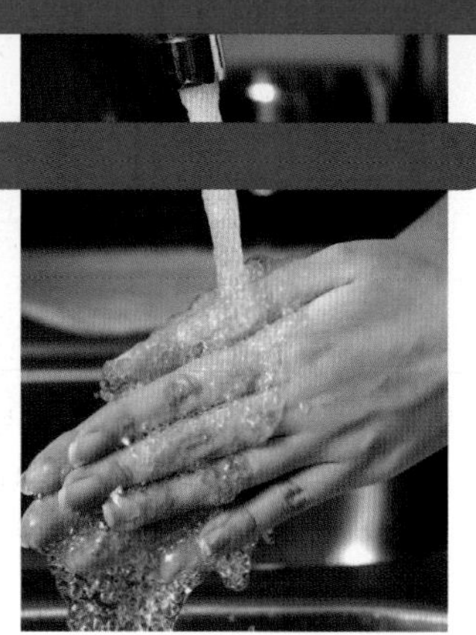

It is very important to prepare food safely in order to reduce the risk of harmful bacteria spreading and growing in food. Harmful bacteria in food can lead to food poisoning. When preparing, cooking and serving food, the following personal hygiene rules should be followed:

- Wash hands regularly, especially before preparing food and eating, and after handling raw foods, going to the toilet, touching waste, coughing and sneezing, handling pets or caring for someone who is unwell.
- Avoid handling food if you are unwell.
- Cover cuts, sores and burns with clean dressings or blue plasters and change these regularly.
- Wear a clean apron. Never prepare food in unclean clothing.
- Remove jewellery before preparing food.
- Avoid touching hair and tie long hair back.

Shopping for food – dos and don'ts

Do ...

- observe the personal hygiene standards of staff handling and serving food, especially the procedures followed for handling both raw and cooked foods.
- report unhygienic practices to the store management or the local Environmental Health Department.
- check that chilled and frozen food cabinets are operating at the correct temperatures and are not overloaded.
- buy chilled and frozen foods last and pack them together, preferably in an insulated bag or cool box.
- get chilled and frozen products home and stored appropriately as quickly as you can.
- pack raw foods, fruit and vegetables away from cooked and ready-to-eat foods.
- pack foods that bruise or damage easily above other foods.

Don't ...

- buy cans or packets of food that are damaged or have been opened.
- buy products from counters where raw and cooked foods are displayed and stored together.
- buy products that have exceeded the 'use by' date.

FOOD STORAGE

Proper storage of food is an important part of reducing the risk of food poisoning. Follow instructions to make sure that foods are stored in the correct place, at the correct temperature, for the correct length of time.

Most pre-packed foods carry either a 'use by' or a 'best before' date. Understanding these date marks is an important part of storing foods correctly.

Keep fruit and vegetables in the salad drawer at the bottom of the fridge. Raw meat, poultry and fish should be covered and kept on the bottom shelf, separate from any ready-to-eat foods.

Use by	Best before
This date mark appears on the labels of highly perishable or high-risk foods. These foods go off quickly and generally must be stored in a fridge or a freezer that is operating at the correct temperature. The coldest part of a fridge should be at no more than +5°C. A freezer should be at –18°C or below. Food must be eaten by the 'use by' date. After this date the food is likely to become unsafe to eat and could cause food poisoning.	This date mark will generally appear on the label of low-risk foods that can be safely stored in a cupboard. The date indicates how long the food will be at its best. Most foods will remain safe to eat after this date, but the quality may be affected.

FOOD PREPARATION

- Wash and dry hands thoroughly before handling food.
- Keep raw and cooked food apart at all times.
- Ideally use separate chopping boards for raw and cooked foods.
- Thoroughly wash root vegetables, such as potatoes, leeks and carrots, before use, as they often have traces of soil on them.
- Avoid preparing food for yourself or others if you are ill.
- Always follow instructions carefully when defrosting and cooking pre-packaged frozen foods.
- Always follow label instructions and recipes for cooking times and temperatures.
- Cook all foods until they are piping hot.
- Once they are cooked, keep foods covered and piping hot, above 63°C, until it is time to eat them.
- Keep prepared cold foods in the fridge until it is time to eat.
- Reheat foods to a core temperature of 70°C for at least two minutes.
- Do not reheat food more than once.

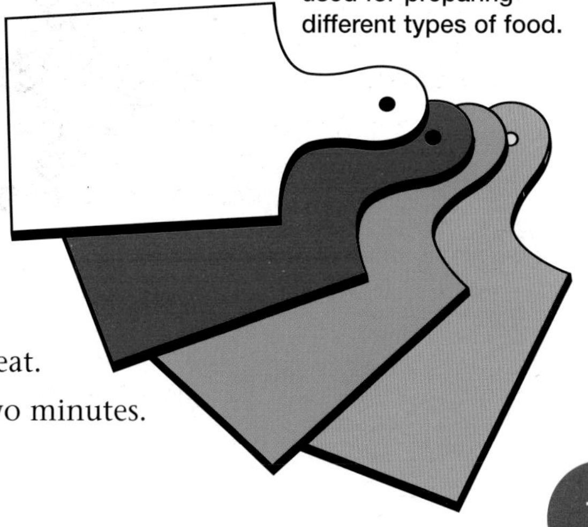

Different-coloured chopping boards can be used for preparing different types of food.

AGES AND STAGES

Babies

Babies are at greater risk of illness than adults, because their immune systems are less developed. Therefore, extra care must be taken when preparing, cooking and serving food for babies.

- All equipment for feeding a young baby should be washed and sterilised, using sterilising solution or a steam steriliser.
- Only cooled, boiled water should be added to baby foods, milks and other drinks.
- Foods should be cooked thoroughly until piping hot and cooled rapidly until comfortable to eat.
- Eggs should be cooked until they are solid.
- Leftover portions should be disposed of rather than stored in the fridge, as saliva from the baby's mouth can cause bacteria to grow in unused portions of food.
- Keep the kitchen extra clean – especially the floor where babies love to crawl.
- Wipe high chairs, bibs and eating areas before and after every meal.

Older people

Older people are also more vulnerable to food poisoning. Extra care should be taken with hygiene and food preparation to minimise older people's risk of coming into contact with food poisoning bacteria. Treatment should be sought if they do develop symptoms of food poisoning.

Pregnant women

Pregnant women should not eat unpasteurised milk and cheeses; soft, mould-ripened cheeses; pâtés; raw or partially cooked fish and shellfish. They should only eat eggs that have been cooked until both the yolk and the white are solid, or use pasteurised egg products. (See pages 24–27 for more information.) If using ready-prepared meals, they should ensure that these are heated thoroughly – at 70°C for at least two minutes – until piping hot throughout.

FOOD POISONING BACTERIA

Table 8.1 (pages 77–78) gives information about the main food poisoning bacteria. It includes the symptoms, likely food sources and methods to help avoid food poisoning.

ACTIVITY 1

Design a series of posters that promote food safety advice in relation to:

- personal hygiene
- food purchase
- food storage
- food preparation
- ages and stages.

ACTIVITY 2

Design an interactive activity for Year 8 pupils, to make them more aware of personal hygiene when preparing food. Call the activity 'Grime Scene Investigation'. You may structure it as a game, quiz or role play.

Table 8.1: The main food poisoning bacteria

Food poisoning bacteria	Symptoms	Food sources	Method of control
Listeria	• Mild flu-like symptoms such as fever, muscle aches and sometimes nausea or diarrhoea. • There can be more serious complications such as headache, stiff neck, confusion, loss of balance, convulsions, blood poisoning or meningitis. • Pregnant women, the elderly and people with weakened immune systems are more susceptible to listeria. • Listeria is particularly dangerous in pregnancy as it can cause miscarriage, premature delivery or severe illness in the baby when it is born.	• Unpasteurised cheeses • Soft, mould-ripened cheeses • Uncooked meats • Cold cuts of meat • Smoked salmon • Pâtés • Ready meals and ready-to-eat foods such as pre-packed sandwiches	Listeria bacteria can grow at low temperatures, including below 5°C. They are destroyed by cooking food thoroughly and by ***pasteurisation***. • Thoroughly cook raw food from animal sources, such as beef, pork, or poultry. • Thoroughly wash raw vegetables before eating. • Keep uncooked meat separate from all other foods. • Avoid unpasteurised milk or foods made from it. • Wash hands, knives and cutting boards after handling uncooked foods. • Pregnant women should avoid eating: - ripened soft cheeses such as Brie, Camembert and the blue-veined types such as Danish Blue or Stilton - any type of meat-based pâté. • Pregnant women should reheat ready-made foods until piping hot, rather than eat them cold.
Salmonella	• Symptoms normally take 12 to 48 hours to develop and may include fever, diarrhoea, vomiting and abdominal pain. • Symptoms usually last for four to seven days and clear up without treatment, but treatment for dehydration may be required. • Young children, the elderly and people whose immune systems are not working properly have a greater risk of becoming severely ill.	• Poultry • Raw meat • Eggs • Unpasteurised milk • Raw, unwashed vegetables	Salmonella bacteria are destroyed through cooking and pasteurisation. • Keep raw food, especially poultry, away from cooked and ready-to-eat foods. • Ensure chicken and other meats are thoroughly cooked until piping hot in the centre to above 63°C. • Always wash hands after handling raw chicken and other raw meats. • If suffering from food poisoning do not handle food until 48 hours after symptoms have stopped. • Individuals infected with salmonella should be particularly careful with personal hygiene, including washing their hands properly after going to the toilet, to avoid spreading infection to others.

Table continues on page 78

Table 8.1 continued: The main food poisoning bacteria

Food poisoning bacteria	Symptoms	Food sources	Method of control
Staphylococcus aureus	• Symptoms can occur soon after eating contaminated food and include severe vomiting, diarrhoea and abdominal pain. • The illness is usually mild and generally lasts no longer than two days.	• Foods most at risk of contamination by staphylococcus aureus are those that are made by hand and require no cooking, such as prepared sandwiches, desserts and cream products. • Cooked meats • Poultry • Unpasteurised milk	Staphylococcus aureus bacteria contaminate food and produce toxins. Food poisoning is caused by eating food containing the toxins. Staphylococcal toxins are resistant to heat and cannot be destroyed by cooking. The bacteria often live on the skin of hands and the nose. If foods are then handled, and not stored properly, the bacteria are able to grow and produce toxins in the food. • Keep very high standards of personal hygiene. • Do not eat, smoke, cough or sneeze in food rooms. • Keep food handling time to a minimum. • Ensure hot food is stored above 63°C. • Keep food refrigerated. • Do not prepare or serve food for others if you have wounds or skin infections on your hands or wrists. • Keep kitchens and food-serving areas clean.

Health inspectors check the safety of the kitchen of a burger restaurant.

ACTIVITY 3

a In pairs, use the internet to research a recent newspaper article which highlights an incident of food poisoning in the UK.

b Present your key findings to the class.

ACTIVITY 4

a Put your answers to these questions in a table like the one below.
- Can I reheat last night's Chinese takeaway, to eat today?
- How do I defrost a chicken safely?
- My shopping has been in the boot of my car all afternoon. Can I safely put away the fridge/freezer food I bought, to use later?

b Design three more questions.

c Collect and record expert food safety advice from:
- www.eatwell.gov.uk/keepingfoodsafe/?lang=en
- www.safefood.eu

Your response	The expert's response

PROTECTION OFFERED TO CONSUMERS

The Food Safety (Northern Ireland) Order 1991 protects consumers from poor standards of food hygiene and the risk of food poisoning. The law is enforced by Environmental Health Officers.

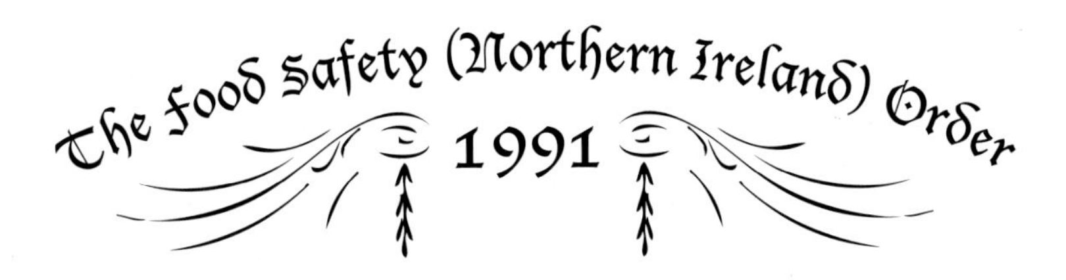

This Order makes it an offence to produce, treat or alter food in any way that could endanger health or to sell food that:

- is unfit for human consumption
- has been declared injurious to health
- is so contaminated that it would be unreasonable to expect consumers to eat it in that state
- is not of the nature, substance or quality demanded by the consumer
- is falsely or misleadingly labelled or presented.

The Order provides enforcement authorities with powers to:

- issue improvement notices
- inspect and seize suspect food
- issue emergency prohibition notices and orders.

(Source: *GCSE Guide to Consumer Organisations and Legislation*, CCEA/Consumer Council for Northern Ireland)

ACTIVITY 5

A local Environmental Health Officer is coming to your class to explain his or her role in protecting consumers in relation to food safety. As a class, decide on a list of appropriate questions to ask.

ACTIVITY 6

a Write down four hygiene rules to follow when preparing food, to help prevent food poisoning.

b Claire is expecting her first child. Her doctor has advised her about the dangers of listeria and salmonella food poisoning. Discuss this advice.

c Jenny, 19 years old, is a full-time student living away from home. She does her shopping weekly. Explain four points she should consider when storing her food, including how she should store and use frozen food.

d Outline the role of an Environmental Health Officer in enforcing legislation.

Each council has an Environmental Health Department, which employs Environmental Health Officers who try to make sure that the council's area is a healthy place to live, work and play. One of the most important roles of an Environmental Health Officer is to maintain high levels of food safety. Environmental Health Officers have the power to inspect food businesses to make sure that they comply with the food safety legislation. If a consumer has a complaint about food quality, food safety, food poisoning or unclean food premises, they should contact an Environmental Health Officer for help and advice.

Chapter 9

Creativity and food

In this chapter you will learn about developing skills, using equipment and using ingredients creatively. After studying this chapter, you should be able to:

- demonstrate a range of skills in the preparation, cooking and presentation of food
- select and use kitchen equipment and processes safely
- creatively respond to food trends when preparing, cooking and presenting food.

DEVELOPING SKILLS

Home Economics promotes and develops a unique range of skills. As a student of GCSE Home Economics, you need to consider how confident you feel about your skills in preparing, cooking and presenting food. Activity 1 helps you to do this.

ACTIVITY 1

Complete an audit or self-evaluation of your practical skills. To help you identify the skills you have and where there are gaps, make a 'Know', 'Want to know' and 'Learned' (KWL) grid like this.

Know	Want to know	Learned
Make pastry using rubbing in method	*Make pastry using the food processor*	*Made bacon and mushroom strudel using pastry made in the food processor*

As the course progresses, and you acquire new skills, you can return to your grid to fill in the 'Learned' column.

Hopefully you have been motivated to study Home Economics by a genuine interest and passion for food. We encourage you to participate in food preparation regularly, both at school and at home. Preparing food is a rewarding experience and an essential skill to learn for life. Also, your practical food preparation skills are continually assessed throughout this course. Informal assessment takes place when your teacher sets activities, such as to plan, make and evaluate a meal, or to modify a recipe for a particular need. Formal assessment takes the form of a Diet and Health controlled assessment task (40 per cent of the GCSE course). This task has three aspects, as shown in Table 9.1.

Table 9.1: The three aspects of the controlled assessment task for the Diet and Health section of your GCSE course

Planning activity	Practical activity	Evaluation activity
• Reasons for choice • Ingredients list • Equipment list • Shopping list • Time plan	• Organisational skills • Selection of ingredients and equipment • Time management • Food handling skills • Practical outcome • Presentation and standard of finish	• Planning • Suitability of choice of dishes • Practical work • Strengths • Weaknesses • Improvements

RECIPES

Successful practical work is linked to well-developed practical skills, but don't forget the importance first of all of choosing an appropriate recipe. A recipe is a detailed set of instructions for preparing a dish. Most recipes have these parts:

- the name of the recipe
- a list of ingredients (type and amount)
- the method (the procedures to follow to make the dish)
- suggestions (about serving, garnishing, cooking times, temperatures, adaptations).

It is important to:

- read the recipe thoroughly before you begin to cook, to ensure that you are adequately prepared
- weigh or measure ingredients accurately, especially when baking. For dry ingredients, use scales, a tala measure or measuring spoons. To measure liquid ingredients, use a measuring jug on a flat surface and read at eye level.

Recipes often include food processing terms, such as those below. Developing an awareness of these will improve your confidence and help make decisions about practical work easier.

Common abbreviations in recipes

Degree Celsius	°C
Gram	g
Kilogram	kg
Litre	l
Millilitre	ml
Tablespoon	tbsp
Teaspoon	tsp

Food processing terms

Beat	to mix ingredients rapidly until they are combined
Bind	to bring ingredients together
Blend	to mix ingredients evenly together
Chop	to cut ingredients into pieces
Coat	to cover with a thin layer
Cream	to beat butter and sugar until light and fluffy
Crush	to grind an ingredient into small pieces
Dice	to cut into cube-shaped pieces
Fold	to add an ingredient to a mixture carefully and lightly
Garnish	to add to a finished dish to improve its flavour or appearance
Glaze	to brush food with egg or milk before baking to add colour
Grate	to shred an ingredient using a grater
Julienne	to cut into long thin matchstick strips
Knead	to stretch and shape dough until smooth
Marinate	to place food in a marinade before cooking to add flavour
Mix	to combine ingredients together
Purée	to process food until smooth
Rub in	to mix fat into flour lightly using fingertips
Shred	to cut or tear an ingredient
Sift	to pass an ingredient through a sieve to remove lumps or aerate
Slice	to cut food into thin pieces

PRACTICAL SKILLS

This spider diagram shows the range of skills you are expected to demonstrate in preparing, cooking and presenting food.

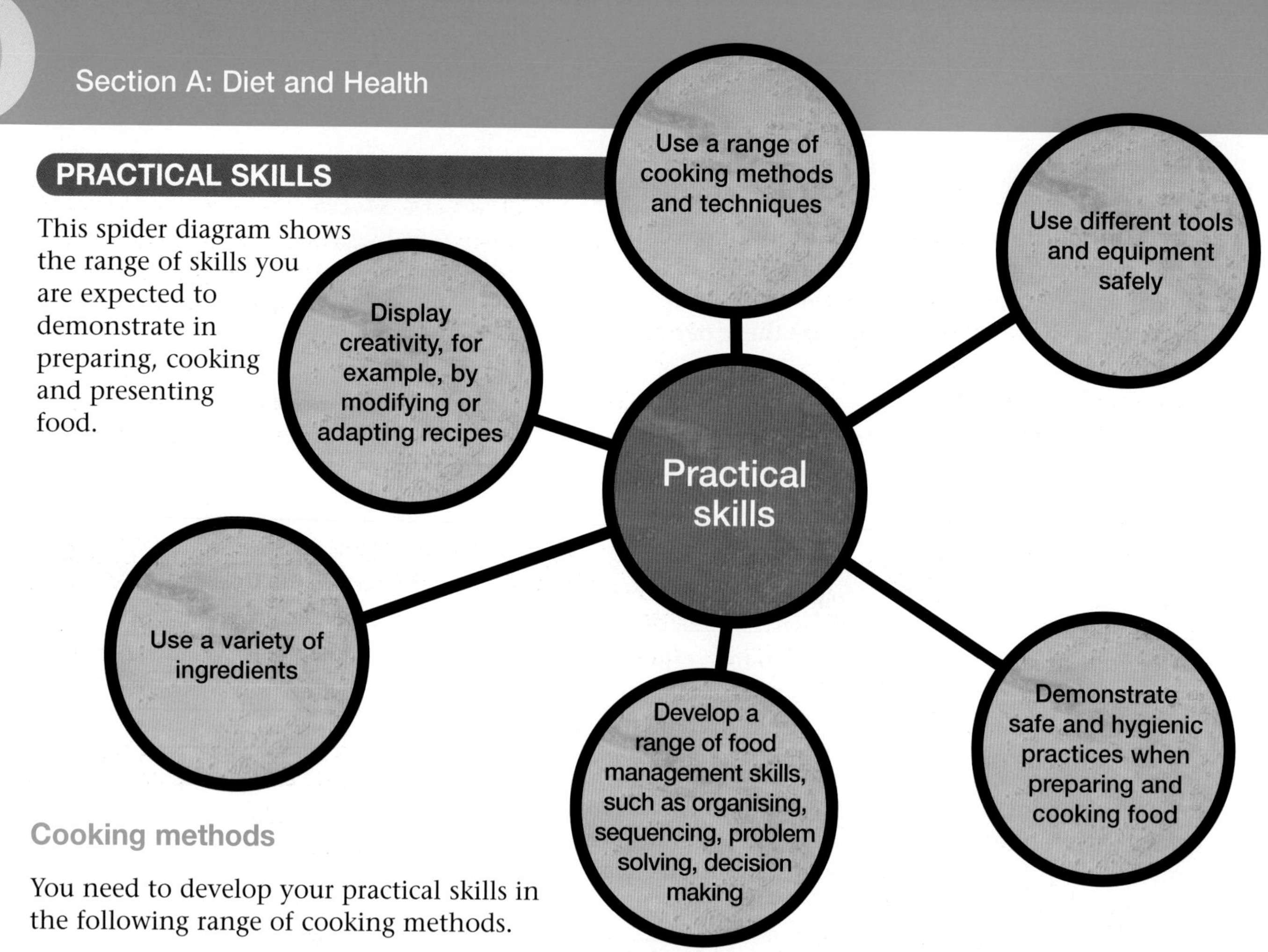

Cooking methods

You need to develop your practical skills in the following range of cooking methods.

Baking	cooking using dry heat in an oven, for example, cakes, bread, biscuits
Boiling	cooking in liquid at or above boiling point (100°C), rapid surface movement
Frying	cooking foods in fat or oil at a high temperature: - shallow frying in a pan using a small amount of fat/oil - deep-frying in a pan using a large amount of fat/oil - dry-frying foods containing fat/oil in a non-stick frying pan - stir frying quickly in a wok, using a high heat and a small amount of fat/oil
Grilling	cooking food using dry heat, using the grill or a grilling machine
Microwaving	cooking, heating or reheating food in a microwave
Poaching	cooking gently in liquid below boiling point
Roasting	cooking in the oven, for example, meat, fish, vegetables
Sautéing	cooking rapidly in a small amount of fat or oil
Simmering	cooking in liquid just below boiling point, gentle surface movement
Steaming	cooking in steam produced from boiling water

Using equipment and appliances

Your practical work should demonstrate an awareness of new developments regarding cookery tools and equipment. Your ability to use a wide range of appropriate equipment and appliances safely and hygienically is an assessable skill. It is important that you display increasing independence in the selection and use of a range of equipment. Examples of equipment to consider are listed below.

ACTIVITY 2

a Select a recipe and present it creatively, with annotations identifying all the equipment and appliances used to make it.

b Highlight one major piece of equipment or appliance and explain five factors that should be considered for its safe and appropriate use.

CAN YOU USE THIS EQUIPMENT?

- Can opener
- Chef's blowtorch
- Colander
- Colour-coded chopping boards
- Flour dredger
- Food scissors
- Garlic crusher
- Grater
- Juicer
- Measuring tools, e.g. scales, tala measure, measuring spoons
- Oven trays and cookware, e.g. cake or muffin tins
- Pastry brush
- Pestle and mortar
- Range of knives, e.g. cook's knife, paring knife, vegetable knife
- Range of saucepans, e.g. frying pan, griddle pan, wok
- Rolling pin
- Sieve
- Spatula
- Tongs
- Vegetable peeler
- Whisk
- Zester

CAN YOU USE THESE APPLIANCES?

- Blender
- Bread maker
- Electric can opener
- Electric juicer
- Electric mixer
- Electric wok
- Freezer
- Fridge
- Food mixer
- Food processor
- Grill
- Hand blender
- Health grill
- Hob
- Kettle
- Microwave
- Mini chopper
- Oven
- Rice cooker/steamer
- Slow cooker
- Smoothie maker
- Toaster

ACTIVITY 3

a Select and evaluate a piece of equipment or an appliance which features a recent technological development, for example, microwave multi-steamer, micro-plane grater, non-stick cookware, flexible silicon-based bakeware. You could refer to catalogues or websites such as Lakeland or Argos and consider some of the following criteria to help you complete your evaluation:

- cost
- durability
- ease of use
- storage
- cleaning.

b Can you think of any other criteria?

Food preparation skills

Some examples of food preparation skills include:

- peeling and slicing fruit/vegetables
- cutting meat
- crushing garlic
- making stock
- combining ingredients to make a marinade.

The diagram below shows how food preparation skills range from basic to highly competent.

ACTIVITY 4

Select a recipe to use for a poster about food preparation and cooking skills. Create the poster by placing the recipe at the centre, surrounded by labels showing the range of skills that you would demonstrate by making the dish.

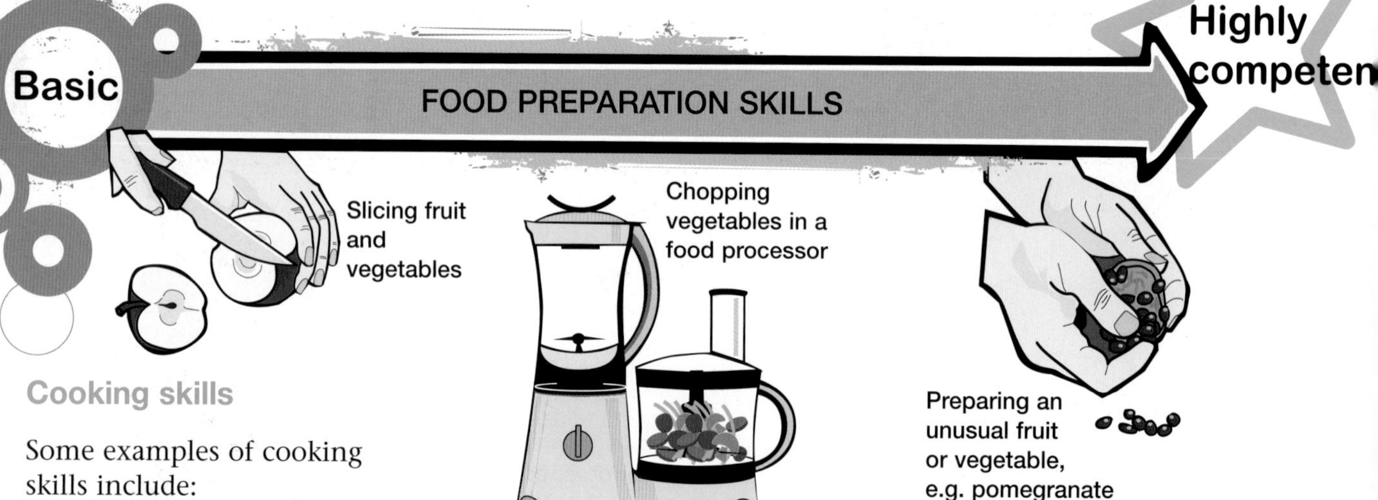

Cooking skills

Some examples of cooking skills include:

- making soup
- baking bread/scones/cakes
- making sauces
- cooking rice, pasta, potatoes, pulses or couscous
- using pastry.

The diagram below shows how cooking skills range from basic to highly competent.

Development of skills

As GCSE Home Economics is a two-year course of study, you should focus on the progression and development of your practical skills. The photographs here show how specific recipes allow you to demonstrate an extensive range of practical skills.

Pasta with tomato and basil sauce (Basic)

- Cooking pasta
- Preparing and cooking sauce
- Garnishing with fresh basil

3 skills

Beef stroganoff with herby pasta

- Cooking pasta
- Preparing and cooking meat
- Being creative, using pappardelle pasta instead of boiled rice
- Garnishing with fresh herbs

4 skills

Lasagne (Highly competent)

- Making meat sauce
- Cooking fresh pasta
- Being creative, adding new ingredients for texture and flavour (e.g. spinach and pine nuts)
- Making a cheese sauce using roux/all-in-one method
- Garnishing with fresh herbs and vine tomatoes

5 skills

Fruit salad (Basic)

- Peeling and slicing fruit
- Presentation and finish

2 skills

Fruit crumble

- Peeling and slicing fruit
- Making custard
- Rubbing in crumble topping
- Presentation and finish

4 skills

Fruit meringue pie (Highly competent)

- Making pastry in food processor
- Blind baking pastry
- Using interesting ingredient (e.g. passion fruit)
- Thickening fruit gel with cornflour
- Making meringue
- Presentation and finish

6 skills

ACTIVITY 5

Using the five sections of the 'eatwell plate' (page 6), complete a table, like the one below, identifying interesting and unusual examples of foods from each food group which you could use in future practical work to make your work more creative.

Creative use of ingredients

As your practical skills develop, so too should your approach to selecting and using ingredients which reflect current food trends. To be aware of current food trends it is useful to:

- watch cookery television programmes
- read cookery books
- review food websites
- visit supermarkets
- talk to people with an interest in food
- try new or different foods if you get an opportunity to eat out or travel.

Interesting and unusual foods to use in future practical work

Bread, rice, potatoes and pasta	Fruit and vegetables	Meat, fish, eggs and beans	Milk and dairy foods	Foods high in fat and/or sugar
Couscous	Sweet potato	Chickpeas	Goat's cheese	Extra virgin olive oil

PRESENTATION OF FOOD

We often judge the quality of food by how it looks and it has been said that we first taste food with our eyes. Plain, clean cookware is often the most effective base for showing food that is to be photographed.

Salmon fillet with lemon and dill sauce.

ACTIVITY 6

a In small groups, identify a range of resources, for example, recipe books, food magazines, websites and television cookery programmes, to investigate how recipes are presented.
b On separate post-it notes, write three key factors that influence your decision when selecting recipes, for example, the inclusion of colourful photographs such as the one on page 86.
c As a class, use the post-its to complete a priority pyramid on poster paper, which can be displayed in your classroom and inform future practical work.

Garnishes and accompaniments

A wide range of garnishes and accompaniments are used by restaurants, celebrity chefs and food magazines to make their food look more appealing. Examples for soup include:

- **Garnishes**: crème fraiche, sour cream, pesto, vegetable crisps, croutons, olive oil, chives, fresh herbs
- **Accompaniments**: bread sticks, wheaten bread, corn bread, cheese twists, pesto scrolls, herb scones.

Can you identify any others?

ACTIVITY 7

Food styling involves making food look appealing so that it can be used in a recipe book, magazine or advertising campaign. A gourmet food magazine has employed you to produce a photograph for their publication.
a Identify and select a recipe.
b Identify a plate and background detail.
c Identify garnishes.
d Plan practical work.
e Carry out practical work.
f Present and photograph the dish.
g Download and manipulate the photograph and print final copy.
h Evaluate photograph (e.g. the quality of presentation and photograph).

ACTIVITY 8

a In pairs, select a soup recipe and prepare, garnish and present the soup. (The soup can be served with an accompaniment, to increase the range of skills displayed, and interesting ingredients can be used to make the dish more creative.)
b Photograph and evaluate the finished dish, in terms of aesthetic appeal.

EVALUATING PRACTICAL WORK

Try to treat each practical class as an important learning experience and make an effort to include enough time to evaluate your work on a regular basis.

Learning to evaluate

Evaluating practical work does not just mean looking at the presentation and finish of food on the plate. It should also include a review of your skills and planning and the processes you have followed. However, that does not mean that every evaluation you do has to be detailed and comprehensive. Sometimes you can focus your evaluation on one specific skill, for example, time management or creativity.

Evaluation is a difficult skill to acquire and takes practice to do well. To complete a balanced evaluation you need to identify:

- ☐ strengths
- ☐ weaknesses
- ☐ next steps or suggestions for improvement.

Sensory vocabulary

To review practical work successfully, consider the descriptive language to use when evaluating your work. Words such as 'nice', 'good' and 'lovely' do little to describe what a dish looks or tastes like. The poster on page 89 is from the British Nutrition Foundation and shows a range of vocabulary that you could use to describe the sensory properties of odour, appearance, taste and texture.

ACTIVITY 9

As a class, complete a card ranking activity to develop a range of criteria suitable for evaluating practical work. This can then be displayed in the classroom to assist you when completing future evaluations.

ACTIVITY 10

As a class, complete a photo journal/collage of practical work which can be used to evaluate the presentation skills of the group.

ACTIVITY 11

a Review a food magazine or cookery book and select two illustrations of recipes that appeal to you.
b Use the sensory vocabulary poster from the British Nutrition Foundation to identify and discuss how colour, texture and shape have been presented to optimise the visual appeal of each recipe, encouraging you to want to cook it.

ACTIVITY 12

a Select and annotate a recipe, showing how you would modify the ingredients and/or food preparation techniques to enhance the nutritional value of the dish.
b Prepare the modified recipe.
c Evaluate the sensory appeal of the completed dish.

SENSORY VOCABULARY

Sensory evaluation involves using one or more tests to determine different characteristics of food such as appearance, odour, taste and texture. A wide range of vocabulary is used to describe sensory characteristics of food products.

ODOUR

The nose detects volatile aromas released from food. An odour may be described by association with a particular food, eg herby, cheesy, fishy. The intensity can also be recorded.

aromatic
floral rotten
perfumed acrid musty
fragrant scented pungent

APPEARANCE

A product's size, shape, colour and surface texture can be described, eg large, small, oblong, square, yellow, pink, rough.

stringy
heavy flat
fizzy crystalline wet
cuboid fragile dull

ɩour and taste
ɾk together to
ɔduce a flavour.
ese words
ɩy be used to
ɔcribe either
our or taste
food products

bland
rancid tart
acidic strong
citrus mild spicy
tainted weak
savoury

These words may be used to describe either appearance or texture of food products.

firm
flaky crisp
fluffy dry crumbly
lumpy smooth
hard mushy
sticky

TASTE

sweet cool bitter zesty warm
hot tangy sour sharp
rich salty

The tongue can detect four basic tastes: sweet, sour, salt and bitter. Tastes may be described by association with a particular food, eg meaty, minty or fruity. The intensity can also be recorded.

TEXTURE

brittle rubbery short gritty
clammy close stodgy
bubbly sandy tacky
tender waxy
open soft

Texture may be assessed through touch. When food is placed in the mouth, the surface of the tongue and other sensitive skin reacts to the feel of the surface of the food. Different sensations are felt as the food is chewed.

BRITISH Nutrition FOUNDATION

MAFF
Ministry of Agriculture Fisheries and Food

Chapter 10

Being an effective consumer

Section B: Consumer Awareness

In this chapter you will learn about being an effective consumer. After studying the chapter, you should be able to:

- identify who is a consumer
- explain the rights and responsibilities associated with being an effective consumer
- explore the barriers that may prevent individuals from being effective consumers, including:
  - disability
  - age
  - ethnicity
  - knowledge
  - resources
- explain how the following legislation protects consumers when buying goods and services:
  - the Sale and Supply of Goods Act 1994 (as amended by the Sale and Supply of Goods to Consumers Regulations 2002)
  - the Consumer Protection (Distance Selling) Regulations 2000
  - the Unfair Trading Regulations 2008.

A consumer is anyone who buys a product, or uses a service, in either the ***public sector*** or the ***private sector***. So, as bus users, pupils, tenants, shoppers, savers or internet users, we are all consumers, in many ways. We live in a consumer-driven society, and are exposed to an ever-changing range of 'must have' ***consumer durables***.

Our role as a consumer is affected by a range of factors, such as:

CONSUMER RIGHTS AND RESPONSIBILITIES

As with any role, being an effective consumer brings rights and responsibilities, as shown in Table 10.1.

ACTIVITY 1

Using Table 10.1 as a starting point, explain how you can be a responsible consumer when buying goods or choosing services.

Table 10.1: The rights and responsibilities of consumers

Rights	Responsibilities
• Right to information, which is clear, reliable and available in alternative languages and formats. • Right to fair treatment. All groups should be equally well served. • Right of access to services, which are inclusive, user-friendly, easily understood and welcoming. • Right to choice (usually related to competition in the marketplace), so consumers can compare and choose the best deal for their need. • Right to redress. Support is given for consumers who need to make a complaint, especially if they don't have the time or skills to do so. • Right to representation: to be consulted and heard.	• Responsibility to read information carefully (including the small print). • Responsibility to know their consumer rights. • Responsibility to complain effectively. • Responsibility to be an ethical and environmentally aware consumer. • Responsibility to manage and budget money wisely and to avoid unnecessary and wasteful buying. • Responsibility to claim reasonable compensation if things go wrong.

BARRIERS

The following are some barriers that may prevent individuals from being effective consumers:

- disability (physical and learning)
- age (younger and older)
- ethnicity (language and culture)
- knowledge (education, numeracy, literacy)
- resources (location – rural or urban, time, finance).

ACTIVITY 2

In groups, take on the role of reporters for a community newspaper to research and write an article called 'What's stopping you?', explaining what prevents people from being effective consumers. Each group could focus on one of these types of barrier:

- disability
- age
- ethnicity
- knowledge
- resources.

Consumer proficiency

Consumer proficiency includes knowing about your consumer rights and responsibilities; being aware of where to find expert consumer advice; and being able to deal confidently with issues, such as complaining about faulty goods or poor service and making your voice heard.

The Consumer Council for Northern Ireland has found that, in general, consumer proficiency is less well developed among young people and older people. A 2003 study showed that people from minority, ethnic and disability groups and those living in areas of social need also tend to be less consumer proficient.

CONSUMER LEGISLATION

Table 10.2 outlines some of the legislation created by parliament to protect consumers when buying goods and services.

Table 10.2: Laws that protect consumers buying goods and services

Legislation	Main features	Protection for consumers	Points to remember
The Sale and Supply of Goods Act 1994 (as amended by the Sale and Supply of Goods to Consumers Regulations 2002)	You are entitled to expect that any goods you buy from a trader are: • of satisfactory quality • fit for any particular purpose made known to the seller • as described.	If you've bought something not of satisfactory quality, not fit for a particular purpose or not as described, the law gives you a number of remedies. If you complain to the retailer within a reasonable time, you are entitled to a full refund. However, the law does not say what a 'reasonable time' is. Each case may be different. So the sooner you make your complaint, the better. Once you go beyond a reasonable time to reject the goods, you are only entitled to claim compensation. You can also claim for any consequential losses that result directly from the goods being unsatisfactory. You can also ask, in the first instance, for a repair or replacement. Such repair or replacement has to be carried out or provided within a reasonable time and without any great inconvenience to you. The retailer has to bear any costs, such as for transporting the goods. However, the retailer can refuse either one of these remedies, if it can be shown that the other one would be less costly. If a quick and trouble-free repair or replacement is not possible, you can ask for a full or part refund. Any benefit you may have had from the goods already will be taken into account in deciding the amount of the refund.	You have no real grounds for a complaint if you: • were told about the fault before you purchased the item • examined the item when you bought it and should have seen the fault • made a mistake when purchasing the item • simply changed your mind about the item.

ACTIVITY 3

You have purchased a product from a local retail outlet. Unfortunately, the product is faulty and you have been advised to write a letter of complaint to the Customer Services manager. Write the letter, using the correct layout for a formal letter and making sure that you include:

- accurate detail about the nature of your complaint
- specific details of how legislation is relevant to the complaint
- expectation of appropriate redress.

ACTIVITY 4

Discuss the legislation that protects consumers who shop online.

Table 10.2 continued: Laws that protect consumers buying goods and services

Legislation	Main features	Protection for consumers	Points to remember
The Consumer Protection (Distance Selling) Regulations 2000	These regulations give consumers rights when they shop via the internet, TV or telephone or from a catalogue or magazine. Consumers are entitled to clear information – before they order – about: • the supplier's name/address • cost of the goods • delivery costs and arrangements • how to pay • how to cancel.	These regulations entitle customers to cancel an order within seven working days (the first day being the day after you receive the goods); and to a full refund if the goods or services are not delivered within 30 days.	• Certain items, such as perishable goods (e.g. flowers, fresh food) and personalised goods, cannot be returned. • If a consumer has bought a service, it cannot be cancelled once it has started.
The Unfair Trading Regulations 2008 (This legislation replaced the Trade Descriptions Act 1968)	This legislation introduces a general duty on businesses not to trade unfairly. It helps to clarify consumers' rights and facilitate cross-border trade by establishing common EU-wide rules against aggressive or misleading marketing. The regulations list 31 banned activities, which include: • visiting a consumer's home and refusing to leave until having a signed contract • telling a consumer that if he or she does not buy, the trader's job or livelihood will be in jeopardy.	Consumers are given the same protection against illegal business practices and rogue traders whether they buy from the shop around the corner or from a website in another member state of the EU. If a trader misleads, behaves aggressively or otherwise acts unfairly towards consumers, the trader may face action by enforcement authorities.	

ACTIVITY 5

Invite a guest speaker from the Trading Standards Department to inform you about how the Unfair Trading Regulations 2008 protect consumers buying goods and services.

What influences shopping?

Section B: Consumer Awareness

In this chapter you will learn about factors that influence shopping. After studying the chapter, you should be able to:

- discuss the factors that influence shopping:
  - cultural
  - economic
  - environmental and ethical
  - personal
  - physiological
  - psychological
  - social
- evaluate these shopping options for different types of consumers:
  - independent shops
  - internet
  - mail order
  - markets
  - shopping channels
  - supermarkets
- discuss the impact of marketing on the choice and management of resources
- discuss the impact of changing lifestyles on the choice and management of resources.

The choices people make about what to buy are influenced by various factors. To start this chapter, we look at these different factors, and give some examples of how they influence shopping.

THE INFLUENCE OF CULTURAL FACTORS

Culture can be described as the beliefs, customs and behaviour of a particular group of people. The culture of a group of people can determine what they wear and eat, how they speak and where they live and travel. Here are two examples of culture affecting shopping habits.

Examples of how cultural factors influence shopping

- Individuals who hold strong beliefs about green issues and take an active role in protecting the environment would consider energy efficiency and the potential for recycling when they purchase new electrical goods such as a fridge freezer.
- People who live in Mediterranean countries are known to value the quality of the food they eat. They often grow fruit and vegetables at home and avoid convenience foods, preferring to cook with raw ingredients. In these countries, food shopping is carried out mainly at small independent shops, such as delicatessens, bakeries and fishmongers, rather than at large supermarkets

NORTHERN IRELAND

ACTIVITY 1

As an adolescent living in Northern Ireland, you are a member of Northern Irish culture and a member of teenage culture. How does this affect your shopping habits?

HOW ECONOMIC FACTORS INFLUENCE SHOPPING

Economic factors have a huge influence on shopping. During periods of economic growth, when wages increase, access to ***credit*** is easy and consumer confidence is high, retailers make large ***profits*** as people shop more frequently and often buy on impulse. It is very different during periods of economic decline. ***Disposable income*** decreases, the ***cost of living*** increases and shopping patterns become more focused, as consumers must ensure that they meet their needs before they spend on wants.

ACTIVITY 2

Complete a list of 'top ten tips' to help consumers get value for money when shopping for food.

Examples of how economic factors influence shopping

- When consumer confidence is high, due to economic growth, there is an increase in buying on credit. Many families buy luxury items, such as a holiday, fridge freezer or furniture, using ***interest-free loans*** which are offered either in store or via credit card deals.
- People's income decreases for various reasons, for example, because of unemployment or ill health (which stops them working) or when they retire. For many consumers a drop in income means they need to reduce their expenditure. They may review their use of services, such as gym membership, cable television or internet provision and 'shop around' for better deals.

ENVIRONMENTAL AND ETHICAL FACTORS

We have a responsibility to consider environmental and ethical issues when buying products or using services. We need to think about the impact of the product or service on the environment. For example, does it use a lot of energy? Can it, and its packaging, be recycled? If it is food, is it ***organic***? In the case of fish, is it ***sustainable***? We also need to think about the people involved in making or providing the product or service. Are they treated fairly? Has a positive or negative impact been made on their culture or workforce? Has child labour been used?

ACTIVITY 3

Research ***fair trade*** and evaluate buying fair-trade products as a means of being an ethical consumer. Websites that could help in your research are:

- www.fairtrade.org.uk
- www.cafod.org.uk
- www.co-operative.coop/food/ethics/
- www.traidcraft.co.uk
- www.oxfam.org.uk/shops/content/fairtrade.html

Examples of how environmental and ethical factors influence shopping

- Many retailers have introduced 'Bags for Life' to encourage consumers to recycle and reduce the amount of plastic carrier bags going to landfill.
- Clothing brands that rely on child labour have been highlighted in the press and consumers have been encouraged to stop buying the clothes.

PERSONAL FACTORS THAT INFLUENCE SHOPPING

Shopping decisions are influenced by the consumer's personal characteristics and circumstances – age, likes and dislikes, occupation, lifestyle and amount of 'free' time. These factors tend to change at different stages of the lifespan. For example, think what the personal factors might be of the two people in the pictures here.

Full time student, part-time job

Married with teenage children, full-time job

ACTIVITY 4

a Complete a shopping profile of a particular consumer at a specific stage of the lifespan. You could carry out an interview or survey to find out what is purchased, where, when and why, and how it is paid for.

b Compare your findings with those of a classmate who has chosen a different stage of the lifespan.

c Do you think your shopping profiles are representative of the lifespan stages?

Examples of how personal factors influence shopping

- A student at school may quickly eat a packed lunch or canteen meal, at a set time. A business person may entertain clients over a leisurely meal at a restaurant.
- A consumer's interest in technology and branding may affect their choice of mobile phone.

ACTIVITY 5

Discuss how personal factors influence shopping habits.

THE INFLUENCE OF PHYSIOLOGICAL FACTORS

Physiological factors relate to the maintenance of the body and the prevention of disease. The influence of physiological factors on shopping depends on consumers' interest and motivation to take care of their well-being. When shopping for food, someone with a dietary disorder, such as diabetes, is strongly motivated to make healthy choices. However, while most consumers know that good health is important, many are not influenced by this when they shop.

ACTIVITY 6

a Evaluate the use of vitamin supplements. You may want to complete a table, with 'Advantages' in one column and 'Disadvantages' in another.

b To extend this activity, consider the advantages and disadvantages of using vitamin supplements in the context of a specific stage of the lifespan, such as pregnancy, childhood or older adult.

Examples of how physiological factors influence shopping

- Some consumers need to avoid substances to which they are allergic. They may need to shop in particular stores which stock the food or clothing brands that are suitable for them.
- Consumers concerned to achieve a healthy weight may evaluate different weight loss services, such as a gym, personal trainer, slimming club, or GP.

THE INFLUENCE OF PSYCHOLOGICAL FACTORS

As consumers we have many characteristics in common, but we are also all individuals. Our attitudes, personality (for example, whether we are self-confident, sociable, aggressive, etc), emotions and body image all inform who we are and what we do. Psychological factors like these affect what, when, where and why we buy products and services.

Examples of how psychological factors influence shopping

- A sociable person may eat out regularly or meet friends for coffee or drinks, influencing the type of food and drink bought and the frequency of purchase.
- Individuals with negative feelings about their body image may find it stressful to shop for clothes in stores and instead choose to shop online.

ACTIVITY 7

a Complete an online personality test. For example, go to www.bbc.co.uk/science and search 'personality tests'.
b Use the results of your test to assess your shopping habits, for example, how, when, where and why you shop.

SOCIAL FACTORS THAT AFFECT SHOPPING

The effects that other people have on us are called social influences. Most obviously, we are influenced by our family, friends and any groups we identify with, for example, church groups or sports teams. Many shopping decisions are a mixture of social interaction and individual decision-making. Shops often use social factors in their marketing campaigns.

Examples of how social factors affect shopping

- Adults are often loyal to the supermarket chain and the brands that were most frequently used by their family when they were growing up.
- Teenagers often take on the attitudes and values of their peer group and this can impact on the type, style and brand of clothing they purchase and wear.

ACTIVITY 8

Consider the different groups you belong to and describe how this influences your shopping habits. Try to consider both the products you buy and the services you use.

SHOPPING OPTIONS

Table 11.1 highlights the advantages and disadvantages of different shopping options available to consumers.

Table 11.1: The advantages and disadvantages of different shops and shopping methods

Type of shop	Advantages	Disadvantages
Independent shops	• Offer personal and friendly service. • Usually in residential areas for ease of access. • Usually sell things in small quantities, helping customers to save money and reduce waste.	• May be more expensive. • Stock may not be rotated or replaced regularly. • The range of products for sale may be limited.
High street chain stores	• Uniform store layout makes shopping easier. • Stock a wide range of items. • Buy in bulk and can offer consumers value for money.	• Can be very busy, making shopping stressful. • Customer service can be impersonal. • Lack individuality.
Supermarkets	• ***Economy of scale*** means they can offer value for money. • Offer an extensive range of products, services and facilities. • Offer a range of financial incentives, e.g. loyalty cards.	• Usually situated out of town, so a car or public transport is essential for access. • Often busy and large, making shopping time-consuming. • Special offers can encourage buying on impulse, increasing expenditure.
Shopping centres	• Offer a range of shops under one roof. • Extended opening hours and extensive parking improve accessibility. • Often well designed and luxurious, making shopping an enjoyable experience.	• If situated out of town, a car or public transport is essential for access. • Often busy, which can make shopping stressful. • Can be very large, which can make navigation difficult and shopping time-consuming.

Table 11.1 continued: The advantages and disadvantages of different shopping methods

ACTIVITY 9

a Discuss the advantages and disadvantages of two shopping options for consumers at different ages and stages.
b Evaluate the internet as a method of shopping for busy families.

Method of shopping	Advantages	Disadvantages
Internet shopping 	• Products or services can be accessed and evaluated in the comfort of the consumer's home. • Available 24 hours a day. • Extensive range of products or services can be purchased, including specialist and overseas brands.	• Consumers need access to the internet and to know how to use it and shop online. • Consumers must have a debit or credit card to buy online. • Goods or services can be time-consuming to compare, and may be misrepresented.
Mail order 	• Convenient for those who have difficulty accessing shops. • Payment can often be spread over a number of months. • Large or heavy items can be delivered directly to a specified address.	• It can be difficult to judge quality from a catalogue. • Consumer needs to be at home to accept delivery. • May have to pay for postage to return unwanted goods.
Going to markets 	• May be cheaper than shops. • Local products are often available. • Friendly, sociable shopping experience.	• Packaging and labelling may not be available to help determine quality. • Often outdoors so can be affected by weather conditions. • Usually operate early in the morning or on specific days only.
Shopping channels 	• Can see products being demonstrated by experts. • Products can be viewed in the comfort of own home. • Entertaining.	• Persuasive selling can encourage impulse buying. • Can be difficult to determine quality. • Returning products that are unsatisfactory can be time-consuming and expensive.

THE IMPACT OF MARKETING ON THE CHOICE AND MANAGEMENT OF RESOURCES

Marketing is a complex process which ultimately persuades consumers to buy a particular product or service. Each day we are bombarded with an extensive range of marketing strategies, which companies hope will encourage us to spend money. Most marketing strategies begin with the principles of the marketing mix or 'Four Ps':

- PRODUCT: What is it?
- PRICE: What does it cost?
- PLACE: Where will we sell it?
- PROMOTION: How will we tell consumers it exists?

Marketing companies consider the Four Ps and use this to inform their decisions about the type of marketing strategy they will use to maximise sales.

Advertising

One marketing strategy used to promote products and services is advertising. Table 11.2 gives examples of some of the places where it appears. Advertising is everywhere!

Table 11.2: Where advertising appears

Contexts	Examples
• In the media	Newspapers, magazines, television and cinema
• Outdoors	Billboard posters, transportation (e.g. bus shelters), illuminated signs
• ***Direct mail***	Leaflets, fliers and vouchers
• Sponsorship	Sports events, entertainment events and charitable events

The main purpose of advertising is to develop increased levels of recognition and awareness among consumers. The marketplace is saturated with products and services, so how do consumers choose one from another? Whatever they are promoting, from sports cars to underwear, advertisers carefully select images, language, music and celebrities to make their products appealing to their target consumers. Advertisements often provide limited factual information and instead rely on matching up with consumers' desires, dreams and aspirations.

Age is widely used for targeting purposes. The advertising of breakfast cereals is a good example of this. Children are targeted by the use of fun products and animated characters, while a different type of advertising campaign is used for cereals aimed at the body-conscious female market.

ACTIVITY 10

a Analyse a television advertisement you enjoy. Your analysis could include:
- the name of the product or service advertised
- the features of the product or service that are highlighted
- the target audience for the advertisement
- when the advertisement is shown
- what advertising strategies are used (for example, language, music, slogans, appealing images, stereotypes)
- how effective the advertisement is in promoting the product or service.

b Discuss the impact of advertising on consumers.

Selling techniques

Selling techniques are designed to add value to the shopping experience by encouraging consumers to buy from a particular store, try a new product and repeat purchase. Examples of selling techniques include:

- **Packaging**: bright, colourful, glossy packaging creates a perception of quality and increases the likelihood of purchase.
- **Loss leaders**: stores may sell a product at a 'special offer' price, which is so low that sales of this particular product make the store a loss rather than a profit. However, the special offer encourages consumers into the store and it is hoped that, while there, they will buy other products too.
- **Own brands**: stores offer their own brands as cheaper alternatives to branded products.
- **Price checking**: shops highlight products that they are offering at lower prices than other stores, to show that they are giving better value for money.
- **Financial incentives** (see right).
- **Beacon colours**: stores use bright colours to highlight special offers.
- **Pester power**: products are marketed specifically at children, often with endorsements from TV/cartoon characters.
- **Store layout**: almost every shop uses strategies regarding its layout to encourage consumers through the door and get them to stay for some time, because the longer they stay, the more they spend. Examples are shown on pages 102–3.

Financial incentives

SPECIAL OFFERS!

Financial incentives are promotions offered to help consumers save money. They are an important marketing strategy for stores as they increase profitability.

- PRICE PROMOTIONS may take the form of a discount to the normal selling price of a product. These include 'buy one get one free', or more product at the normal price – for example, '20% extra free'.
- CROSS-BRAND PROMOTIONS are where different brands are sold together, as part of a special offer. They are a form of price promotion as they offer consumers the opportunity to buy a product and sample the complementary product free. For example, buy one perfume/aftershave and get a sample of a new perfume/aftershave free.
- MONEY-OFF VOUCHERS are often used to offer a current or future discount to the consumer. This is a highly versatile form of financial incentive as vouchers can be included on the pack, to encourage repeat purchase, in direct mail or in newspaper advertisements.
- LOYALTY CARDS, offered by some shops, allow consumers to collect points which are then used to give them money-off vouchers or to offer them a choice of gifts.
- A GIFT WITH PURCHASE is sometimes given. For example, spend £25 on groceries and get a free set of barbecue utensils. This style of promotion is often used with luxury goods, with the gift hopefully enhancing the quality of the purchase.

ACTIVITY 11

Consumers like to get value for money when shopping for food. Research and discuss a range of financial incentives currently offered by different shopping options, for example, supermarket, chain store and independent shop.

STORE LAYOUT

In 2005, *Which?* magazine published an article about the strategies used by supermarkets to make customers want to buy and 'cram their trolleys full'. Here is what they reported about the layout of supermarkets.

1 At the entrance

- Just inside the supermarket there is some clear space, to let customers adjust to the atmosphere.
- The heating may blow warm air on to customers, which is psychologically welcoming.

2 Look to the right

- Apparently, 75 per cent of customers look right when they enter a store, and so supermarkets put their best offers on the right after the front door.
- Also, magazines may be displayed in this area, to the right of the front door. This encourages people to stay and browse, before they do the rest of their shopping.

3 Fruit and vegetables

- Fruit and vegetables are placed near the front of the supermarket. Consumers associate fruit and vegetables with freshness and quality, and having them at the front of the store has a positive effect on sales.

4 On the shelf

- People tend to look at things on a shelf from left to right. So, for example, in a display of cans of soup, the most expensive ones are positioned on the right.
- The cheapest variety is put either on a high shelf or on a low shelf, to prevent customers from seeing it too easily.
- Items that appeal to children are displayed on low shelves.

ACTIVITY 12

a Explain how the selling techniques shown on these two pages have influenced your family's purchases when shopping for food at a large supermarket.
b Which other examples of selling techniques can you think of?

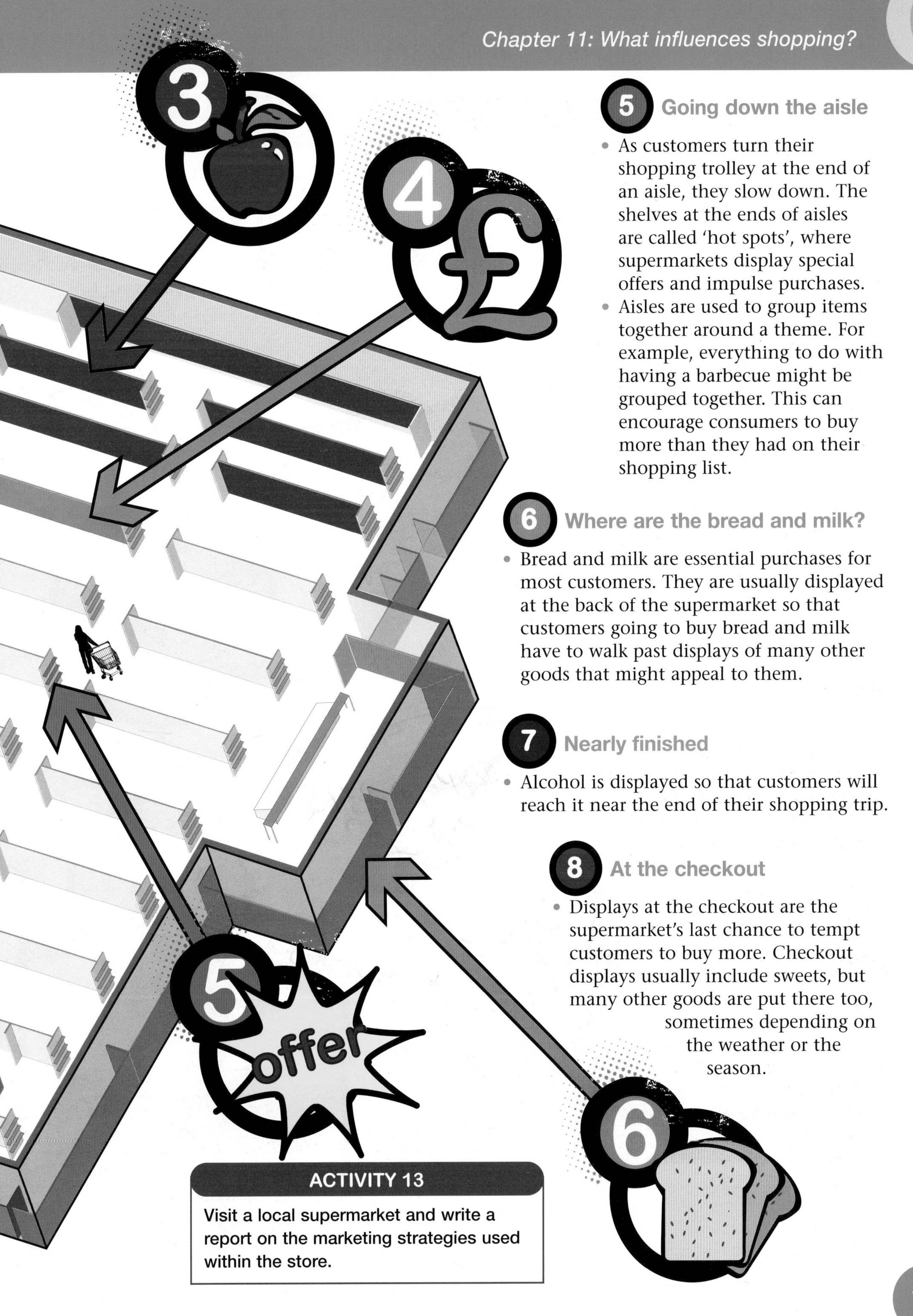

5 Going down the aisle

- As customers turn their shopping trolley at the end of an aisle, they slow down. The shelves at the ends of aisles are called 'hot spots', where supermarkets display special offers and impulse purchases.
- Aisles are used to group items together around a theme. For example, everything to do with having a barbecue might be grouped together. This can encourage consumers to buy more than they had on their shopping list.

6 Where are the bread and milk?

- Bread and milk are essential purchases for most customers. They are usually displayed at the back of the supermarket so that customers going to buy bread and milk have to walk past displays of many other goods that might appeal to them.

7 Nearly finished

- Alcohol is displayed so that customers will reach it near the end of their shopping trip.

8 At the checkout

- Displays at the checkout are the supermarket's last chance to tempt customers to buy more. Checkout displays usually include sweets, but many other goods are put there too, sometimes depending on the weather or the season.

ACTIVITY 13

Visit a local supermarket and write a report on the marketing strategies used within the store.

THE IMPACT OF CHANGING LIFESTYLES ON THE CHOICE AND MANAGEMENT OF RESOURCES

The products we buy and the services we use are also affected by changes in lifestyle. A change in lifestyle often occurs as a result of a change in circumstances, such as losing one's job or moving from one stage of the lifespan to the next, for example, from adolescent to adult. The spider diagram below shows some of the lifestyle factors that influence the way we choose our purchases and manage our resources.

ACTIVITY 14

Select a resource – for example, food, mortgage product or credit card – and discuss how people's choice and management of this resource could be affected by the lifestyle factors shown in the spider diagram.

Chapter 12 Money matters

In this chapter you will learn about managing your finances. After studying the chapter, you should be able to:

- explain the importance of budgeting for different individuals and families
- evaluate methods of paying for goods and services
- outline the consequences of poor financial management for different individuals and families
- discuss strategies to enable different individuals and families to manage their finances effectively.

BUDGETING

You need to budget, to balance money coming in (income) and money spent (expenditure). This involves working out carefully what you will need to spend and how much money you have.

Being able to budget is a skill and each individual or family will prioritise spending in different ways. There is no right or wrong way to prioritise, as we all have different needs and wants. It is important to remember that how we prioritise will determine our lifestyle. There is really only one rule: budget for needs before wants.

Needs	Wants
Needs are things you must have to live a basically healthy life: for example, food, clothing, transport and electricity.	Wants are things you would like to have in order to improve your quality of life: for example, eating out, holidays, fashionable clothes, a bigger house or a car.

As consumers, we are constantly faced with various spending dilemmas.

THE IMPORTANCE OF BUDGETING FOR INDIVIDUALS AND FAMILIES

The main reason for budgeting is to avoid ***debt***. A budget also helps people to decide how they can save some money for use in an emergency – for example, to repair their car or an essential appliance such as the boiler, if it breaks down. It is estimated that four out of five people will receive a bill they are not expecting over the next twelve months and that 50 per cent of householders will need to resort to credit cards and overdrafts in order to pay. This is why it is important to budget to set aside money for emergencies.

> 65 per cent of consumers undertake some form of forward planning for household bills and everyday spending. However, almost one in three undertake no planning whatsoever. (*Source:* Consumer Proficiency Research, Consumer Council, 2007)

The Consumer Council for Northern Ireland has produced a leaflet giving detailed advice on how to budget. The front is shown below and the complete leaflet can be found at www.consumercouncil.org.uk/ education/adult-education-training/budgeting-tool.

Home Budget Planner

The Consumer Council

Where does your money go?

Knowing where and how you spend money can help you save. This can help you pay for unexpected bills and plan for occasions like holidays and Christmas.

To create your Home Budget Planner, gather all the paperwork that you need. For example, electricity, phone, gas bills, grocery receipts, bank/credit card statements and all other spending receipts. To make this budget planner work for you, you must work out your total bills, spending and income either **weekly** or **monthly** - stick to this throughout the exercise.

Here is a guide on how to work out your budget:

Calculating Monthly?	What to Do
Monthly bills	Enter amount in 'monthly' column
Quarterly bills (eg telephone)	÷ 3
Yearly bills (eg Christmas)	÷ 12
Weekly bills (eg PAYG Mobile)	x 52 then ÷12

Calculating Weekly?	What to Do
Weekly bills	Enter amount in 'weekly' column
Quarterly bills (eg telephone)	÷ 13
Yearly bills (eg Christmas)	÷ 52
Monthly bills (eg mobile phone)	x 12 then ÷ 52

ACTIVITY 1

a Download the Home Budget Planner leaflet from the Consumer Council and try to complete the home budget for your family.

b Alternatively, create an individual budget based on your income (e.g. from part-time work, pocket money) and expenditure.

ACTIVITY 2

Keep a diary of all your spending for one week. Keep all receipts. Calculate your total weekly expenditure and, from this, design a personal budget.

METHODS OF PAYING FOR GOODS AND SERVICES

Methods of paying for goods and services include:

- cash
- cheque
- debit card
- credit card
- store card
- hire purchase.

Each method has advantages and disadvantages.

Paying with cash

Cash is currency in the form of bank notes and coins. Paying for products or services with cash is quick, efficient and cost-effective as, in some cases, when you pay cash, a discount can be negotiated. As no interest can be charged for cash payments, the price you see is the price you pay. Disadvantages of paying with cash often relate to accessing cash from your bank account and safety issues associated with carrying large sums of money.

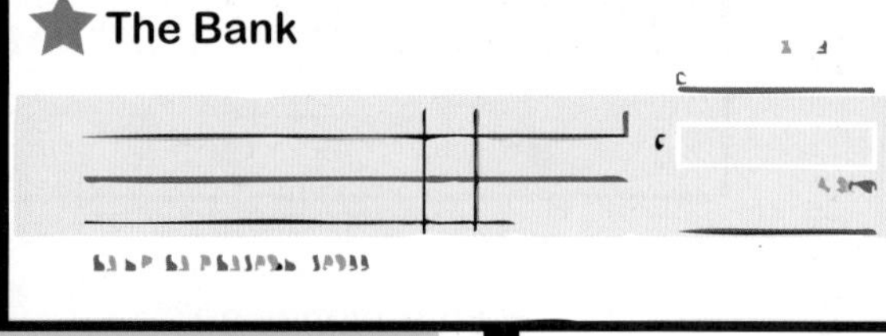

Paying by cheque

A cheque instructs your bank to release funds from your account to a payee (for example, the retailer from whom you purchase a product or service). Cheques are useful for people who do not wish to carry large amounts of cash. They are a flexible method of payment where the exact total cost is unknown beforehand, for example, for the weekly supermarket bill. In order to write a cheque, individuals must have a bank or building society account that is in credit and have been issued with a cheque book and cheque card. Banks charge retailers a fee for every cheque they receive, to cover the banks' processing costs, and some retailers no longer accept payment by cheque.

Paying by debit card

A debit card draws from the funds in your bank account to pay for products purchased or services used. Debit cards are a quick and efficient method of payment. They are cost-effective as they do not usually incur charges or interest for the consumer.

Paying by credit card

A credit card enables a consumer to borrow money from the card issuer to pay for products or services. Card holders receive regular statements of how much they have borrowed and need to repay. Credit cards are quick and efficient and are particularly useful for large or unexpected purchases. The main problem is the high interest charged by the card issuer. Also, a charge may be made for using the credit card, for example, when paying for airline flights online. Payments must be made to the card issuer every month to reduce the outstanding balance. If the balance is not paid in full each month, interest is added, therefore increasing the risk of debt.

Store cards

A store card allows a consumer to borrow money from the card issuer to pay for products or services. Store cards are provided by specific stores, for use in their chains, and special discounts or member benefits may be offered. However, the rates of interest are often higher than for most credit cards. Store cards can encourage impulse buying and excessive spending. Regular monthly payments need to be made to pay off money borrowed on the store card.

Hire purchase

Hire purchase is a credit agreement that allows a consumer to borrow money from the credit provider to pay for a product or service. Large chains, such as furniture and electrical shops and car dealerships, often offer hire purchase as a method of payment. If the hire purchase loan is interest-free and the repayments are planned and monitored effectively, this can be a good way to borrow money. However, the payment schedule must be strictly adhered to or the consumer may end up having to pay the interest for the term of the loan, which could be twelve months or more.

ACTIVITY 3

a Create and complete a table, listing the advantages and disadvantages of each of the payment methods described on pages 108–9. Make your table with three columns, for Payment method, Advantages and Disadvantages.

b Compare a range of credit card deals currently on offer, using an online comparison website such as www.gocompare.com or www.moneysupermarket.com.

CONSEQUENCES OF POOR FINANCIAL MANAGEMENT

Poor financial management means failing to manage your finances effectively. Some of the consequences of poor financial management are shown in this spider diagram.

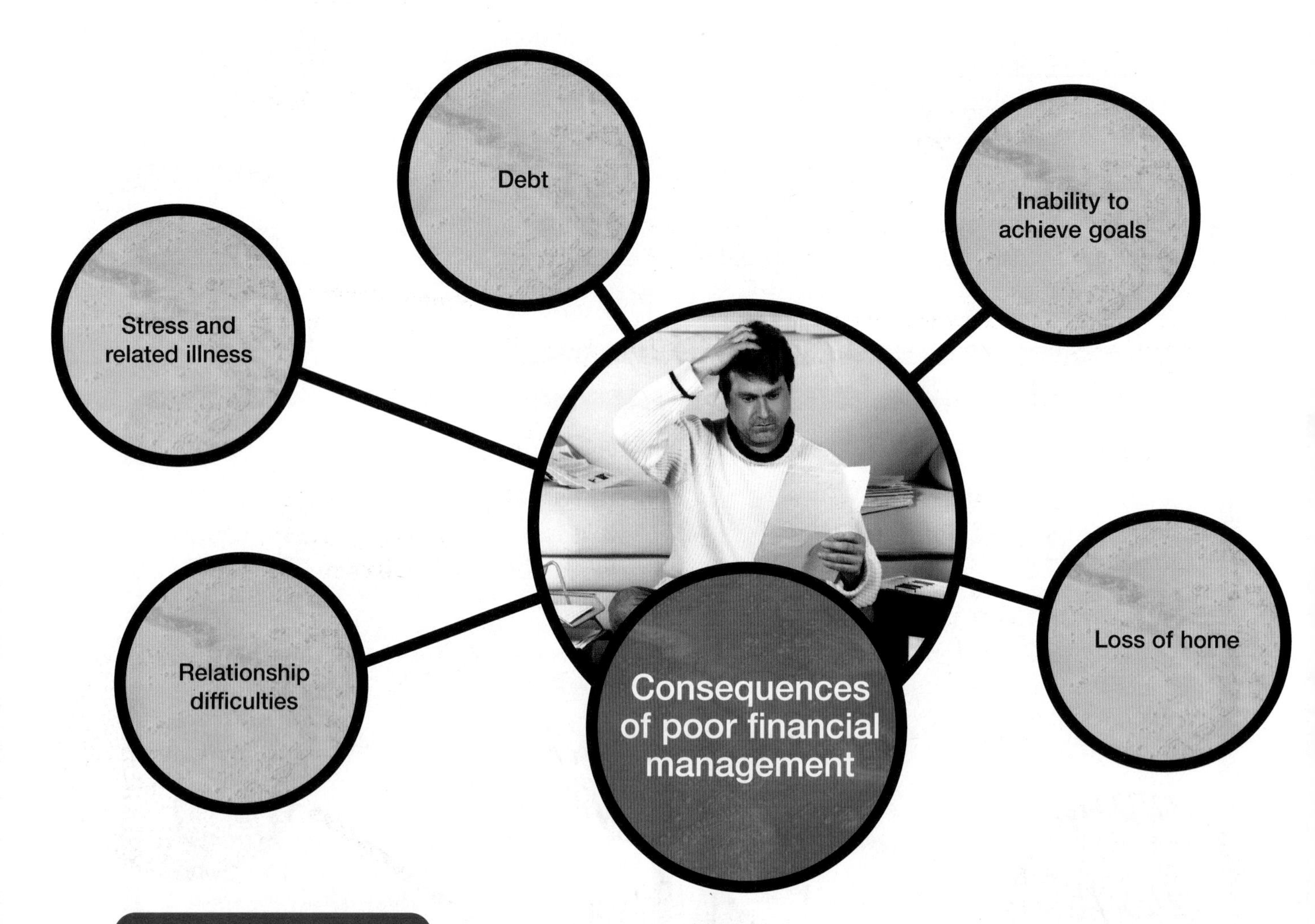

ACTIVITY 4

Create a noticeboard display using newspaper and magazine headlines which highlight some of the consequences of poor financial management.

Strategies to help

The following are a range of strategies that could help people who find themselves in difficulties as a result of poor financial management.

- Discuss problems with family and friends.
- Review spending habits and buying behaviour.
- Design a personal budget.
- Establish regular saving habits.
- Seek professional financial advice.

MANAGING FINANCES EFFECTIVELY

It is important to manage finances effectively to avoid the consequences of poor financial management. Some tips on money management are given in the first of these spider diagrams.

Tips for good money management

- Keep a check on credit card
- Put money to one side for emergencies
- Make allowances for little extras
- Open and check bills and statements
- Stick to the budget and prioritise needs and wants
- Plan budget and monitor it regularly

Signs of poor money management

- No budget planned
- Impulse buying and credit card left unchecked
- Sliding into creeping debt
- Spending on what you can't afford
- Bills and statements unopened and unchecked
- No prioritising of needs and wants

ACTIVITY 5

Justify the importance of good money management.

MONEY TIPS

The leaflet below is based on advice given by the Consumer Council for Northern Ireland.

Curb the urge to splurge

Money-saving methods

1. Take lunch to work at least two to three times a week. This could save you £15 per week, or £800 a year, simply by using what you've already got in the fridge!
2. Plan meals in advance and prepare a shopping list before you go shopping. Studies prove that shoppers without a list buy more items than those who come prepared.
3. Cook meals from scratch to avoid the cost of pre-prepared meals.
4. Do one big food shop once a week.
5. Buy in bulk and split costs with a friend.
6. Think about buying goods second-hand or in charity shops.

ACTIVITY 6

Visit the website of the Consumer Council for Northern Ireland (www.consumercouncil.org.uk) and create an advice leaflet to inform consumers how they can save money in one area – food, motoring or public transport.

1. Buy non-brand products and use money-off coupons.
2. Become a comparison shopper.
3. Price check with other stores.
4. Check the prices of goods on the bottom shelves. Goods at eye level normally cost more money.
5. Do your sums on quantity and pricing.
6. Think: getting 15 or 20 per cent extra or three for two is great BUT only when it's something useful. End-of-aisle displays aren't always a bargain.
7. Ask yourself: do you really need it?

ACTIVITY 7

a Using information from the Consumer Council's 'Money Tips for Parents' leaflet shown above, design a PowerPoint® presentation which could be delivered at a parenting course. You can download the leaflet from www.consumercouncil.org.uk/publications

b Carry out the shoparound quiz on the Consumer Council's website: www.shoparound.org.uk/index.html

ACTIVITY 8

Outline strategies to help families on a limited budget to manage their spending when shopping for food or paying household bills. You can find ideas at www.consumercouncil.org.uk/cost-of-living-consumer-tips

Chapter 13 Wiser buyer

In this chapter you will learn about being a discerning consumer. After studying the chapter, you should be able to:

- evaluate the quality of information available to consumers from:
  - the media: consumer programmes, magazines and newspapers
  - individuals: family, friends and experts
  - the internet
- identify and explain the purpose of safety and environmental information on labels
- justify choices and decisions to develop skills as informed and discerning consumers
- describe the support and information provided for consumers by:
  - Advice NI
  - Citizens Advice
  - Consumer Advice Centre
  - Consumer Council for Northern Ireland
  - Trading Standards Service
  - Which?

INFORMATION AVAILABLE TO CONSUMERS

Consumers are regularly bombarded with information about an extensive range of goods and services. It is often difficult to determine the quality of the information, because there is so much of it. On these two pages we consider the advantages and disadvantages of different information sources.

ACTIVITY 1

a As a class collect a range of samples of consumer information.
b Determine a list of criteria to evaluate the quality of the information. For example: availability, accessibility, relevance, ease of use, reliability, independence/bias.
c In small groups, evaluate one source of consumer information and present a summary of your findings to the class.

ADVANTAGES

- A relatively inexpensive source of information.
- Specialist magazines offer reliable independent advice.
- Information can be kept and used at a later date, for example, when shopping.

DISADVANTAGES

- Some specialist magazines involve expensive subscriptions, which make them inaccessible to some consumers.
- Many magazines are funded by advertising revenue and so it can be difficult to determine the independence of information.
- Many magazines are published with the purpose of entertaining and it can be difficult to obtain factual information.

ADVANTAGES

- Presented in an entertaining format.
- Information is well researched and factual.
- Experts are often used to present specialist information.

DISADVANTAGES

- Information can be of general rather than specific value.
- You have to plan to view programmes of specific interest.
- Information may be presented too quickly to be useful.

ADVANTAGES	DISADVANTAGES
• Broadsheet journalists are often experts in their field, e.g. finance. • Tabloid newspapers can present information in an easy-to-understand format, in user-friendly language. • Inexpensive and readily available.	• There is potential for information to be ***biased*** or sensationalist. • Information is often general rather than specific. • It can be difficult to determine the quality of the information or the qualifications/expertise of the journalist.

ADVANTAGES	DISADVANTAGES
• Relaxed and informal. • You can ask questions to get specific information relevant to your needs. • Another person's experience of using a product or service can be valuable.	• Information can be biased. • The knowledge of family and friends is unqualified. • Information supplied may be inaccurate.

ADVANTAGES	DISADVANTAGES
• Staff who have received training can give specialist information. • Experts can explain technical information accurately, in a way consumers can understand. • Experts can demonstrate how a product or service works.	• The information can be technical and complicated, making it difficult to understand. • Staff can be hard to access when needed, especially in busy shops. • Sales staff may not have received specialist training and information could be inaccurate.

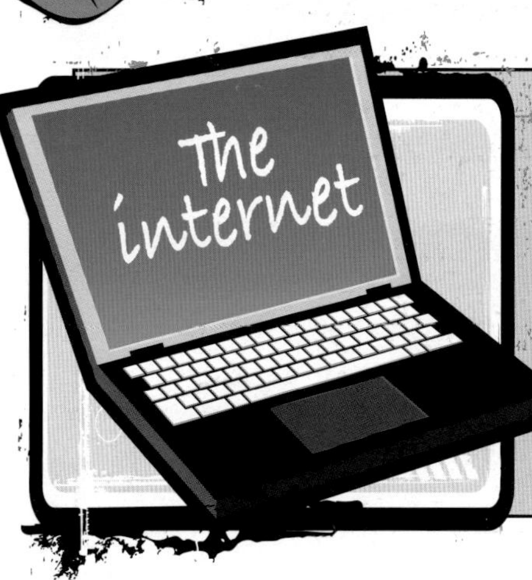

ADVANTAGES	DISADVANTAGES
• Provides access to an extensive range of information. • Information can be accessed in the comfort of your own home. • Quick way to compare products and services from a range of shops.	• Using the internet can be slow and time-consuming. • IT skills are needed to make full use of the internet. • It can be difficult to judge which websites offer reliable information.

SAFETY INFORMATION ON LABELS

Table 13.1: The meanings of safety labels and some examples of where you will find them

Table 13.1 highlights some examples of safety labels commonly found on a range of household products.

Label	What is it?	What does it mean?	Where will you find it?
	The Kitemark	The British Standards Institute (BSI) Kitemark assures consumers that a product is safe and reliable and conforms to relevant safety standards. The symbol shows that the BSI has independently tested the product and given the manufacturer permission to use the mark.	• IT equipment • Gas hob • Car windscreens
CE	The CE mark	The CE mark shows that the product meets European safety/environmental standards. It allows manufacturers to sell their products within Europe.	• Toys • Telephones • Light bulbs
	Harmful or irritant	This label tells consumers that a product may be harmful if inhaled or swallowed. The impact on health could include skin or breathing problems.	• Bleach • Cleaning products • Dishwasher powder
	Toxic	This label tells consumers that a product contains ingredients which would be extremely dangerous if inhaled, swallowed or in contact with skin. If misused, products with this label could cause serious harm or death.	• Bleach • Weedkiller • Paint stripper
	Highly flammable	The product or its fumes will catch fire easily if it is near heat, flames or sparks.	• Fireworks • Aerosol cleaning products • Nail polish remover
BEAB Approved	The British Electrotechnical Approvals Board (BEAB) trademark	The BEAB Approved trademark is an electrical safety mark. It tells consumers that the product has been independently tested and evaluated against European and international safety standards.	• Toaster • Microwave • DVD player

ACTIVITY 2

a Identify other products that have the safety labels shown in Table 13.1.

b Carry out research at home to identify other safety labels. Present your findings to the class, using the same headings as in Table 13.1.

ENVIRONMENTAL INFORMATION ON LABELS

Concern for the environment and an increased awareness of our responsibilities when shopping have increased the demand for environmental labelling to help consumers make informed decisions when choosing products and services. Some of these labels are explained below.

ACTIVITY 3

a Explain the purpose of environmental labelling.

b Evaluate the information presented on environmental labels.

c How does this information help people develop skills as informed and discerning consumers?

The Fairtrade mark

The Fairtrade mark is a registered certification label for products sourced from producers in developing countries. It informs consumers that international fair trade standards have been met with regards to:

- fair prices paid to producers
- community investment
- safe and healthy working conditions
- environmental protection.

The Soil Association symbol

The Soil Association sets standards for organic production and processing, which promote ***biodiversity***, recycling and reduction of waste. Manufacturers and retailers who have met these standards are allowed to use the Soil Association symbol on products they produce and sell. In the case of food products, the symbol means that they have been grown without the use of pesticides and ***artificial fertilisers***.

Energy labels

Energy labels on white goods such as washing machines show how energy-efficient they are, with A representing the most efficient and G the least efficient.

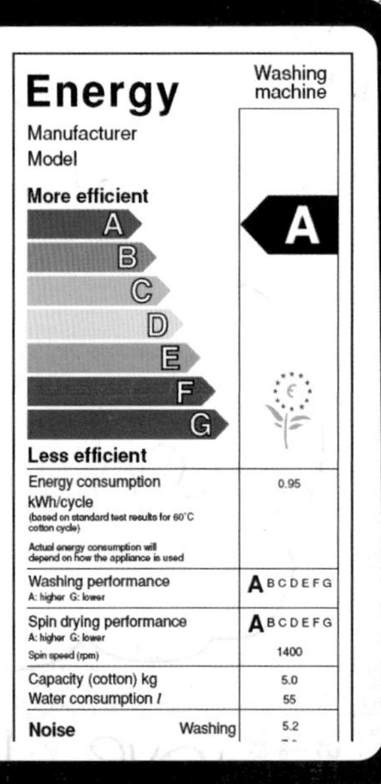

The recycling symbol

The recycling symbol tells consumers that the material used for packaging can be recycled.

ACTIVITY 4

Explain how an energy efficiency label like the one shown above could help consumers to make an informed choice when purchasing a washing machine.

CONSUMER ORGANISATIONS

ACTIVITY 5

Many individuals experience barriers that may prevent them from being effective consumers. Examples could be disability or age (see Chapter 10, page 91). Carry out research to outline the support offered to consumers by specialist organisations such as Disability Action or Help the Aged.

On this page and pages 119–23, we look at organisations that provide support and information for consumers.

Advice NI

Advice NI is a membership organisation which exists to promote, support and develop the independent advice sector across Northern Ireland. Advice NI does not assist consumers directly. It offers training and support for a wide range of independent organisations that do offer advice to consumers, including, for example, Disability Action and Independent Advice Centres.

Advice NI aims to develop an independent advice sector that provides the best possible advice to those who need it most.

How does advice NI inform and support consumers?

Advice NI supports organisations with links to consumers and so, indirectly, it assists consumers.

- Advice NI provides training for National Vocational Qualifications (NVQs) in Advice and Guidance and Wiseradviser, money advice training.
- It offers workshops through its Learning Online website.
- It uses eConsultations to give socially excluded groups the opportunity to highlight issues of concern and participate in debate. These groups include, for example, those living in disadvantaged rural or urban areas, older adults, lone parents, and people with disabilities.
- It offers advice through its website, www.adviceni.net

advice ni
the independent advice network

Consumer Focus

Consumer Focus is a ***statutory organisation*** campaigning for a fair deal for consumers in England, Wales, Scotland, and, for postal services, Northern Ireland. It is a consumer advocacy organisation, rather than an advice agency answering specific consumer queries. This means that it campaigns about a range of consumer issues on behalf of groups of consumers who may not be listened to: for example, older adults. Consumer Focus was created in 2008 through the merger of three consumer organisations – Energywatch, Postwatch and the National Consumer Council. The new approach allows for a more consistent approach to consumer advocacy, with one single organisation speaking with a powerful voice. Its website is www.consumerfocus.org.uk

Citizens Advice

Citizens Advice is a registered charity which helps people to resolve problems with debt, benefits, housing, the law, discrimination, employment and immigration. Consumers can contact Citizens Advice by telephone, in person, and via letter or e-mail.

Citizens Advice aims to:

- ensure that individuals do not suffer through:
  - lack of knowledge of their rights and responsibilities
  - lack of knowledge of the services available to them
  - inability to express their needs effectively
- exercise a responsible influence on the development of social services both locally and nationally.

How does Citizens Advice inform and support consumers?

- Citizens Advice offers free, confidential and impartial advice to consumers about a range of issues, including consumer and employment legislation, social security benefits, money, health, housing rights and legal matters.
- It interviews consumers in person and by telephone.
- It helps consumers to negotiate with companies or service providers.
- It writes letters and telephones companies and service providers on behalf of consumers.
- It helps consumers to prioritise their problems.
- It helps consumers with form filling.
- It represents consumers in court and at tribunals.
- It refers consumers to specialist caseworkers or other agencies when necessary.
- It initiates campaigns to inform people about consumer issues.
- It gives advice through its website, www.adviceguide.org.uk

ACTIVITY 6

Evaluate the information available to consumers who use the Citizens Advice website.

The Consumer Advice Centre

The Consumer Advice Centre is part of the Health and Environmental Services department of Belfast City Council. To use the centre, consumers or traders must work or live in Belfast or be visitors. Advice can be obtained by visiting the centre in person, or by telephone, e-mail or letter. Currently Belfast is the only council area in Northern Ireland that offers a Consumer Advice Centre, covering goods and services bought within the city council area.

The Consumer Advice Centre aims to:

- provide free specialist advice to consumers and traders in Belfast on consumer issues such as faulty goods, shopping complaints, bad service and holiday complaints
- resolve problems through:
  - negotiation – reaching an agreement through discussion and compromise
  - conciliation – working with opposing individuals to bring them to an agreement.

ACTIVITY 7

a Research how to write an effective letter of complaint.

b Produce a fact sheet to be distributed by the Consumer Advice Centre, which would help consumers to write effective letters of complaint to traders.

How does the Consumer Advice Centre inform and support consumers?

- The Consumer Advice Centre provides an advice service where all consumers are treated fairly.
- It advises consumers of their legal rights under civil law, for example, righting a wrong, honouring an agreement, or settling a dispute.
- It gives advice on how to write an effective letter of complaint to a trader.
- It advises on how to follow up a complaint.
- It writes follow-up letters to traders on behalf of consumers.
- It refers consumers to other organisations, such as Trading Standards (see page 122).
- It supports consumers taking their complaint (if under £2,000) to the ***small claims court***.
- It acts as mediator between consumers and traders to achieve a fair solution for all.
- It gives talks on consumer law and consumer rights to schools, voluntary groups, traders and other organisations.
- It provides resources, such as leaflets on credit, environmental issues and legislation.
- It contributes to a quarterly magazine, *City Matters*, on issues relating to consumer advice, for example, on internet shopping.
- It gives advice through its website, www.belfastcity.gov.uk/consumeradvicecentre

The Consumer Council for Northern Ireland

The Consumer Council for Northern Ireland is a statutory organisation set up by the government in 1985 and funded by the Department of Enterprise, Trade and Investment (DETI). Its main role is to promote the interests of all consumers in Northern Ireland.

The Consumer Council for Northern Ireland aims to:

- provide consumer information and skills to all, so that consumers can make informed decisions
- speak up for consumers, to make their voice heard
- ensure that the policy makers in Northern Ireland consider the opinions of consumers when making decisions that affect all people in Northern Ireland.

ACTIVITY 8

Use the Consumer Council for Northern Ireland website to identify a range of issues where the council has recently campaigned on behalf of consumers in Northern Ireland.

How does the Consumer Council for Northern Ireland inform and support consumers?

- The Consumer Council for Northern Ireland provides information on a wide range of consumer issues.
- It undertakes research.
- It produces publications.
- It handles complaints about buses, planes, trains, ferries, natural gas, electricity, coal and water.
- It campaigns on behalf of consumers to improve standards of service and protection.
- It gives advice through its website, www.consumercouncil.org.uk
- It manages a consumer-focused website called Consumerline (see below) at www.consumerline.org

Consumerline

Consumerline is a website (www.consumerline.org) and telephone helpline which provides consumer advice in Northern Ireland. It is a joint enterprise between the Consumer Council for Northern Ireland, which manages the website, and the Trading Standards Service (see page 122), which operates the telephone helpline.

The website provides guidance on a wide range of issues – from travel and transport to money matters and consumer advice.

The telephone helpline deals with consumer issues including complaints about package holidays and defective goods/services. Consumerline advisers advise on legal rights and what to do next and, when appropriate, they pass on the complaint to the Trading Standards Service.

ACTIVITY 9

Visit www.consumerline.org and outline three useful resources available to consumers on the website.

The Northern Ireland Trading Standards Service

The Northern Ireland Trading Standards Service is part of the consumer affairs branch of the Department of Enterprise, Trade and Investment. The role of the Trading Standards Service is to promote and maintain fair trading, protect consumers and enable reputable businesses to thrive within Northern Ireland. The Service is responsible for enforcing a wide range of consumer protection laws, as well as for providing advice and guidance to both consumers and traders.

The aims of the Trading Standards Service are to:

- empower consumers
- ensure that businesses comply with consumer protection legislation
- protect consumers and honest traders against unfair trading
- work in partnership with the business community to maintain good practice.

How does the Trading Standards Service inform and support consumers?

- The Trading Standards Service investigates complaints and collects evidence.
- It checks that goods and services comply with legislation.
- It advises consumers and traders about the law.
- It investigates disputes between consumers and traders.
- It ensures that all goods sold by weight, volume, length or area, are accurately measured.
- It ensures that goods and services offered for sale are accurately described and free from false/misleading descriptions.
- It checks that traders accurately display the price of all goods.
- It attends court and gives evidence.
- It confirms that traders offering credit hold a valid credit licence.
- It ensures that estate agents treat buyers and sellers honestly.
- It ensures that only classified films are offered for sale or rent, and that children are not able to rent or buy films with an adult classification.
- It enforces the Trademarks Act 1994, which prevents the unauthorised use of trademarks and the sale of counterfeit goods.
- It enforces legislation that protects consumers who have either purchased timeshare properties or are seeking redress from holiday companies.
- It investigates complaints about businesses involved in illegal trading practices.
- It delivers presentations to schools, voluntary groups and trade groups.
- It provides a telephone consumer advice service called Consumerline (see page 121).
- It gives advice from its website, www.detini.gov.uk

ACTIVITY 10

a Use the Trading Standards Service website to learn more about its work.
b Report back on a specific issue of interest (a good starting point may be Consumer Affairs > For consumers > FAQs and Some problem areas).
c Invite a Trading Standards Officer to class to answer specific questions about his or her role in informing and supporting consumers.

Which?

Which? is the largest consumer body in the UK, with over a million members. It is a registered charity and completely independent.

The aims of Which? are to:

- promote informed consumer choice in the purchase of goods and services
- raise awareness of consumer rights
- be an advocate for consumers.

Which? magazine is published every month.

How does Which? inform and support consumers?

- Which? publishes a monthly magazine, which is available by annual subscription. The magazine includes product testing, mystery shopping and best buy information on a range of products and services. Topics include computing, cars, food and health, family, greener living, holiday and leisure, photography and video, money, TV, music and radio, and legal rights.
- It provides a website (www.which.co.uk) which offers information on publications, campaigns and services. The website includes a free advice section and a subscription-only reviews section.
- It carries out product testing. A wide range of consumer products are tested (for example, washing machines, digital cameras) to establish which is the 'best buy'.
- It carries out mystery shopping. This is sometimes known as 'situation testing', for example, pretending to be interested in buying a house through an estate agent in order to evaluate the service provided.
- It carries out surveys, collecting the opinions of its members and the general public and using this to inform campaigns, for example, to reduce bank charges.
- It publishes books on a range of topics including careers, family and lifestyle, finance, food, legal advice and property.
- It identifies and gives awards for good practice and good products or services, such as 'retailer of the year'.
- It makes super-complaints. A super-complaint is an action taken on behalf of a large group of consumers about any market that is not working properly for consumers. For example, a super-complaint was made about the Northern Ireland banking sector and unfair bank charges in 2006.
- It presents podcasts to inform consumers about topical consumer-related issues. An example is the Which? cars podcast.

ACTIVITY 11

Describe the support and information provided for consumers by Which?

Strategies for achieving your best

To help you realise your potential and achieve your best in this GCSE course, choose ways of learning that are most useful for the type of learner you are. You may be:

- a visual learner who needs to see information and write it down in order to retain it
- an auditory learner who is very good at remembering information you have heard or discussed
- a kinesthetic learner who retains information best when involved in hands-on activities.

COMMAND WORDS

Become familiar and confident with the command words that may be used in GCSE Home Economics. The words shown in the table below may be used in:

- textbook or classroom activities
- coursework guidelines and assessment criteria
- the written examination.

EXAMINATION RESPONSES

In the written examination you will be required to answer several types of question:

- short factual recall questions – answers to these should be focused and succinct and display your knowledge of the subject area
- extended response questions – answers to these should be structured and display knowledge and understanding of the subject area. There is no need to introduce or conclude your response, as this can often result in repetition
- scenario questions – answers should be in context and clearly linked to the question focus
- data response questions – data, e.g. on credit cards, should be interpreted and discussed.

Remember:

- Read the questions carefully.
- Consider the mark allocation.
- Highlight command words.
- Use subject-specific terminology.
- Keep your answer focused to the question.

Command words and their meanings			
analyse	examine something in detail.	evaluate	judge something, stating advantages and disadvantages.
comment	state a fact or express an opinion.	examine	study something in detail.
compare	examine two or more things, identifying similarities and differences.	explain	make the meaning of something clear.
consider	review the pros and cons of a situation.	identify	name or list.
debate	present different perspectives on an issue.	justify	present an explanation for something.
define	describe something exactly.	outline	set out the main points.
describe	set out the main characteristics of something.	review	examine information for accuracy.
discuss	present relevant points.	state	express clearly.
		summarise	present the main points only.

In GCSE Home Economics there are several opportunities to develop independent learning skills. In particular, the ability to research or debate key issues relating to Diet and Health or Consumer Awareness will help you to address the three assessment objectives and prepare to complete the controlled assessment tasks. For more information refer to pages 4–5.

HOW TO RESEARCH

1. Identify a topic or area of research. It is often helpful and effective to phrase the title of your research as a question.
2. Decide on the type and amount of information you need. Formulate a plan of work. You may want to consider formatting and word limit at this stage.
3. Select information from appropriate sources. You should investigate a range of resources, for example, textbooks, journals, websites, magazines and newspaper articles. It is important to be able to evaluate the quality of the resources, making a judgement about the quality of the information provided. For example, is it current and reliable?
4. Make notes. To do this effectively, ensure that you make notes in your own words. Keep them succinct and focused, writing in the style or format that suits you best. Be subject-specific.
5. Record the sources you are using. Make a note of website addresses, book titles and authors.
6. Reference information accurately. Cite or source any findings you wish to use in your work to avoid plagiarism.
7. Review and refine your work. Spell-check, proofread and review it. Make corrections.
8. Complete the bibliography. This is a list of all the resources you have used to complete your research.

HOW TO DEBATE

1. An issue is researched and a motion (statement to be debated) is formulated.
2. A pair of pupils will support the motion; they will be the proposer and the seconder for the motion. Another pair of pupils will dispute the motion; they will be the opposer and the seconder against the motion.
3. The pupils research the issue and prepare their responses to the motion.
4. To begin the debate, the chair (person in charge) opens the debate, takes attendance and checks who is allowed to vote at the debate.
5. The chair reads out the motion of the debate.
6. The proposer speaks in favour of the motion.
7. The opposer speaks against the motion.
8. The seconder for the motion speaks, followed by the seconder against.
9. The chair opens the motion to the floor. Anyone in the audience may raise their hand and, when given permission by the chair, speak for or against the motion.
10. After everyone has spoken, the chair asks:
    a. the opposer to give a brief summary of why people should vote against the motion
    b. the proposer to give a brief summary of why people should vote for the motion
11. The chair organises a vote, using either a show of hands or a ballot. The votes are recorded:
    a. number of votes in favour of the motion
    b. number of votes against the motion
    c. number of those who have chosen not to vote (abstained).
12. The chair announces the result of the vote and declares that the motion is either passed or defeated.

Glossary

additives: chemicals added to food to improve its shelf life, flavour, colour, texture, appearance, or stability.
amino acids: the basic structural units of proteins.
anaphylactic shock: a sudden severe and potentially fatal allergic reaction in somebody sensitive to a food or substance. Symptoms may include a drop in blood pressure, difficulty breathing, itching and swelling.
antioxidant: a substance that reduces the destructive effects of oxidation in the body, therefore protecting cells from damage by free radicals.
artificial fertiliser: a synthetic chemical substance or mixture used to enrich soil in order to promote plant growth.
atherosclerosis: a condition in which an artery wall thickens as a result of the build-up of fatty materials such as cholesterol.
basal metabolic rate (BMR): the minimum amount of energy needed by the body to maintain life. It includes the energy required to keep the heart beating, sustain breathing, repair tissues and keep the brain and nerves functioning. BMR varies depending on height, weight, age and level of activity.
biased: influenced by a preference for, or dislike of, something.
biodiversity: the existence of a wide variety of plant and animal species in their natural environment.
blood cholesterol levels: the amount of cholesterol in the blood. Cholesterol is a fatty substance found in the blood. It is mainly made in the body and plays an essential role in how every cell in the body works. Too much cholesterol in the blood can increase the risk of heart problems.
blood pressure: the pressure of circulating blood on the walls of blood vessels.
body mass index (BMI): a unit of measurement describing weight in relation to height. BMI is calculated by dividing a person's weight (in kg) by their height squared (m^2). It is used to classify people as underweight, normal weight, overweight or obese.
carotene: a substance that is converted to vitamin A in the liver. It is found mainly in some plant foods, such as carrots, green leafy vegetables and orange-coloured fruits.
complex carbohydrates: a collective name for starches and NSP, which have a more complex chemical structure than sugars (simple carbohydrates).
consumer durables: goods that can last for a relatively long time, such as refrigerators, cars and DVD players.
consumer proficiency: the ability of a consumer to apply knowledge to a range of situations and to deal with them effectively.
convenience foods: commercially prepared food designed for ease of use. Products often require minimal preparation.
coronary heart disease: a condition that can occur when the walls of the arteries become blocked by a build-up of fatty deposits, making it harder for the artery to supply blood and oxygen to the heart.
cost of living: the average cost of the basic necessities of life, such as food, shelter and clothing.
credit: money borrowed to be paid back later. It can take many forms, (e.g. bank loan, credit card) and often incurs interest.
debt: a sum of money owed.
dehydration: a lack of water in the body.
dental caries: the disease process leading to tooth decay.
diabetes: a condition in which the body's normal way of breaking down sugar is not functioning properly. This means the pancreas is not producing any or enough insulin to regulate the amount of sugar in the blood.
direct mail: advertising or marketing material posted to people at home or work, often called 'junk mail'.
disposable income: the amount of money available to spend, after deductions such as tax and National Insurance are taken from an individual's wages or salary.
economy of scale: a decrease in the total cost of manufacturing a product, due to lower costs per unit when larger quantities are produced.
essential fatty acids (EFAs): fatty acids, such as Omega 3 and Omega 6, that must be supplied in the diet as the body cannot produce them.
fair trade: a guarantee that a fair price has been paid to the producer for the produce.
fast food: food that can be prepared and served very quickly. This typically refers to food sold in a restaurant or store and served in a packaged form to take away.
food intolerance: a condition where someone is unable to tolerate certain parts of foods. It is different from a food allergy because the immune system is not involved.
fortified: with particular ingredients added in order to add nutrients or improve flavour.
glucose: a sugar naturally found in honey and the juices of many fruits. Glucose is also the sugar that circulates in the blood.
gluten: a protein found in some cereal grains, especially wheat. People who have coeliac disease are allergic to gluten.
glycogen: a substance found in the liver and muscles that is easily converted to glucose for energy.
grazing: irregular snacking throughout the day.
haemoglobin: the red oxygen-carrying pigment in red blood cells.
heart attack: a sudden illness caused when the arteries supplying blood and oxygen to the heart become blocked.

hypertension: high blood pressure.
immune system: a range of cells that the body uses to protect itself from disease.
insulin: a hormone which the body needs to convert sugar into energy.
interest-free loan: a fixed amount of money that is lent to someone (the borrower), without any fee (interest) being charged.
iron deficiency anaemia: a disease caused by lack of iron, meaning that red blood cells cannot carry enough oxygen around the body.
kilocalories (kcal): 1000 calories, a unit of food energy.
lactation: the process of breastfeeding.
lactose: an extrinsic sugar found in milk and dairy products.
malnutrition: inadequate nutrition – either a lack of healthy foods in the diet, or an excessive intake of unhealthy foods, both of which can lead to ill health.
metabolic rate: the speed at which the body converts food to energy.
metabolism: the process by which food is converted into energy.
non-milk extrinsic sugars (NMES): sugars not found within the cellular structure of food. They are found in honey, fruit juices, table sugar and confectionery.
non-starch polysaccharide (NSP): a type of carbohydrate found in plants. It cannot be absorbed but is needed to keep the digestive system healthy.
nutritional status: the quality of intake of nutrients in the diet.
nutritionists: professionals who study and advise on nutrition.
obesity: a dietary disorder caused when excess kcals are stored as fat, resulting in excessive weight gain. Obesity is classified as a BMI over 30.
Omega 3 and Omega 6: types of essential fatty acids (see above).
organic: produced with restricted use of fertilisers and pesticides.
osteomalacia: pain and bone weakness in adults caused by a deficiency of vitamin D.
osteoporosis: a disease characterised by low bone density and deterioration of the bone tissue, which results in fragile bones and increased risk of fracture.
overweight: a dietary disorder caused when excess kcals are stored as fat, resulting in weight gain. A BMI of over 25 is classified as overweight.
pasteurisation: a heat treatment to destroy bacteria, extend shelf life and make food safer to eat.
peak bone mass: the stage at which bone is strongest, reached at the age of 30–35 years.
pesticides: a range of chemicals used to control contamination caused by pests.
post-menopausal: after the menopause, when menstruation (periods) has permanently stopped.
prebiotics: usually carbohydrate products, such as breakfast cereals rich in soluble fibre, which promote the function of probiotics and help maintain a healthy digestive system.
private sector: part of the economy that is owned and controlled by private individuals and business organisations.
probiotics: products usually in the form of fermented milk or dairy products containing good bacteria which are claimed to improve the health of the digestive system.
processed foods: foods that have been altered through manufacturing procedures.
profit: financial gain, calculated by deducting the costs/expenses from the income of a business.
protein energy malnutrition: a condition resulting from an inadequate intake of protein.
public sector: part of the economy that is owned and controlled by the government.
rehydration: replacing the body fluids which have been excreted from the body.
retinol: vitamin A found naturally in some animal foods, such as cheese, eggs, oily fish and whole milk.
rickets: a softening of bones in children, potentially leading to fractures and deformity. The main cause is a vitamin D deficiency.
saturated fat: fats mainly from animal sources, typically solid at room temperature. Examples include butter and lard.
sensory appeal: how appealing we consider food to be, based on our evaluation of the taste, smell, texture and appearance of an ingredient or finished dish.
shelf life: the length of time that a food or drink is given before it is considered unsuitable or unsafe for sale or consumption.
simple carbohydrates: sugars with a simple chemical structure.
small claims court: court of law for most consumer-related disputes.
spina bifida: a developmental birth defect caused by the incomplete closure of the neural tube in the unborn baby.
statutory organisation: an organisation that must exist by law, such as the police service.
stroke: an attack caused by the blockage of an artery carrying blood to the brain.
superfoods: foods promoted by the media, supermarkets and producers as providing large proportions of important nutrients for good health and offering extra protection against disease.
sustainable: used and managed to ensure that levels of a natural resource are maintained.
unpasteurised: not treated by pasteurisation (see above).
unsaturated fats: fats mainly from plant sources, typically liquid at room temperature. Examples are olive oil and sunflower oil.
vegan: following a diet that excludes animal products of any kind.
weaning: the process of gradually introducing an infant to solid food.

Index